The He Too Movement

Tony Dokoupil

A News man one Can trust

believe!

Thank You

Bernard Johnson

Bernard Johnson

Dedication

I want to dedicate these writings to three of the most significant and loving women in my life. They are as follows: My mother, Lucille Johnson, who always believed in me. Then there is my sister, Rosizean Johnson, who was born ten years before me. She, too, always had my back and looked out for me during good and bad times. And last but by no means least, there is Diane Sentell Johnson, my wife of 30 years, who stood by me through thick and thin and kept a keen eye on me so that no harm would come to me.

I love and miss them all, and may they all rest in peace!

Acknowledgment

I must give a heartfelt shout-out to my daughters, all three of them, because they continually encouraged me to complete these writings even when I had reservations. Without them, this book would not have been finished or published.

Love you all!

About the Author

Bernard Johnson was born in Oklahoma City but was raised in Portland, Oregon. He received his education in Portland and Northern California. While in high school in Portland, Bernard landed a job at a busy Men's Shop and worked there for three years. He began traveling, first to California, then to Hawaii, where he lived for two years, then to Japan, where he lived for three years.

He has six children, three boys and three girls, and now is retired and living in Northern California.

Preface

This Book came into play because, after my first book, Financial Elderly Abuse of A Matriarch, I felt the need to write another because I had too much time on my hands and I needed to continue using my creative thoughts before I lost them by sitting around doing nothing. What triggered the topic was the fact that being a man and seeing how in the last several years men were taking a lot of hits from women about how some men were less than honorable in their behavior towards them.

It occurred to me that it should be known that as bad as man's behavior may seem to be today, we have come light years away from early man and the way they thought about and treated their fellow man, and especially their women. So I believe the truth should be told about how dangerous, brutal, and murderous man was way back then. Hopefully both men and women will learn a lot from these writings and begin treating each other and their children with more love and respect going forward.

Contents

Prehistoric Beast: (RRKD-G)- Rage, Ravage, Kill, Devour-Gene

Primitive Man: (RRKD-G)- Rage, Rape, Kill, Destroy-Gene

Throughout these writings, the words: He Too, Black, & White, are all capitalized by design

Introduction

Looking back, it is hard to believe the tremendous strides and accomplishments that man has achieved ever since he invented the wheel. First, early man had to survive harsh and frigid winters and blistering hot summers. He Too had to avoid being hunted down and eaten by dangerous man-eating predators such as huge snakes, giant birds of prey, sabretooth tigers, and the all-mighty cave bear, who were two times larger than the grizzly bear we see today.

While man dodged or outlived some of those dangers, He Too had to figure out how to become a predator by inventing weapons and becoming hunter-gatherers. Man then began to create tools, carve out dwellings, invent wagons, and claim property and land. Not only did the man claim his property and his land, but He Too claimed his women without the benefit of marriage because there were no marriages. It was like, *'Me, Tarzan, You, Jane, and you're mine.'* If she refused the man would just knock her on her head with his club and drag her to his cave or dwelling.

Early man was very violent, territorial, and possessive, especially regarding his woman. He Too had the primitive variant of the RRKD-G, which made him very dangerous, provoked or not.

As the population exploded on land man learned carpentry and blacksmithing and continued building wagons, rafts, canoes, and then boats. Later came the outriggers which gave him mobility beyond the shores and the ability to reach islands near and far. It wasn't until 3500 B.C. that the man became knowledgeable enough to build ocean or sea-worthy ships. Then, thousands of years later, as they say, "The rest is history!"

Now, with all his wisdom, rage, and weaponry man was ready to conquer the world.

Fast forward several thousand years now that man has weapons of mass destruction. He Too can destroy the whole world.

Act-1: In the Beginning

It has been said and believed by Christians and globally that this Earth began with the Blessing of God. It was fashioned by The Creator of all living things on Earth, including the human race by way of Adam & Eve in the Garden of Eden.

Some historians believe that the Garden of Eden was a land situated somewhere in the region of Mesopotamia in Western Asia near the Tigris and Euphrates Rivers. The two rivers are said to be the water sources for the Garden. These rivers also border and flow through Syria, Turkey, and Iraq.

However, other religions like Islam and Buddhism share slightly different accounts. In fact it is said that physical evidence of Adam and Eve's existence has been uncovered. My question is, how, what, and where is this evidence? I would love to see this physical evidence because all my life I was raised to believe in God and was told the story of Adam and Eve by my mother, Mrs. Lucille Johnson (May she rest in peace). My thing is that during my adult years I have had questions about the truth of the two people: Adam and Eve. In the New Testament Bible Adam and Eve were first mentioned, and in the second reference God created Adam from dust in his own image and placed him in The Garden of Eden.

Shortly after it is said that God created Eve from one or more of Adam's ribs. But the Christian Old Testament does not boldly refer to the Adam and Eve Story. For argument's sake let's say that God placed Adam and Eve in this Garden. Millions believe it to be true, so my question is: Why? He had already created this beautiful Blue Earth with all of its Majestic Mountains and billions of acres of Forest and Greenery all around the planet. He Too created magnificent land animals such as Dinosaurs, Great Apes, Giant Birds flying over the landscape, and huge sea creatures swimming in the seas. God created His very own World-Wide Jurassic Park. There is no way that any of us mere mortals could understand what was in God's mind when He decided to remove those enormous Prehistoric creatures and replace them with the likes of us humans after millions and millions of years.

No clue why He did that(?)

Well I have my own theory on why God might have taken such drastic measures and changed His overall view of what He wanted his New World to look like. I also have my own image of what I think He, The Almighty Himself might look like as well.

When I think of God, who could create such a planet with all of its majesty and beauty, He Too would have to be magnificent in wisdom and stature. Although it is written that God created man in His own image, there is no way that God would appear as a 5-foot-7-inch Napoleon Bonaparte-like figure. Nor could I see Him being this 8-foot-11.1-inch Robert Wardlow-like figure creating such a huge canvas as Earth and calling such astronomical shots.

I imagine God to be this Giant Man-like figure standing at least 1000 times taller than the tallest Dinosaur He created, the Sauroposeidon, which stood up to 30 feet tall. I see this giant of a man with muscular physical attributes with his shoulder-length lamb's wool, salt, and pepper head of hair. I too see his face covered with the same-colored long beard. When appearing in my dreams, He is always dressed the same and wears this long, oversized, beautiful white hooded, Cashmere-looking garment that covers Him from head to toe.

In my mind, He Too wears a huge 24K Gold chain with a Big blue marble pendant hanging from it around His neck. More 24K Gold covers it in the shape of the continents, and He is sporting Gold sandals. It seems to me as if He wears that pendant to represent what He wanted the New World to look like once He placed humans here.

The strange thing about these visions of mine (and there have been many throughout my years) is that I can never determine what nationality He is. It is as if He is colorless. I'm sure that there are as many versions and/or visions of what God looks like as there are people from all kinds of backgrounds who believe in Him. The supra mentioned was just mine. I'm going to go out on a limb here and say 90% of the believers of God also believe Adam and Eve were indeed the first couple He put on this Earth.

Now, on the theory of why God replaced the prehistoric creatures with the likes of Adam and Eve, I would have to assume that He was simply fed up. After more than one hundred million years He just became fed up with all of those giant predators roaming and swimming around His world killing and devouring each other and leaving dead carcasses throughout His beautiful landscape. Far be it for me to know what was on God's mind; all I can do is assume that He felt it was time for a change in scenery – a species change if you will. He wanted a species that looked more like Himself to have a crack at helping Him realize His dream of what He wanted his new World to look like going forward. So

He decided to pick up a huge meteorite and thrust it through the galaxy toward His planet Earth. His aim was true and that was what caused the extinction of all of His prehistoric dinosaurs, making way for His next experiment - the human race.

Act-2: The Other View

On the other side of the Creation Coin some skeptics further suggest that The Garden of Eden was never an actual physical place here on Earth at all. They say it was an extraterrestrial space in the universe where the Gods hang out and call all the shots from.

They say it wasn't until the Supreme God, our God, came down and placed Adam in a garden that He named after the space from which He came. Whichever religion or belief one chooses to subscribe to, Christianity, Catholicism, Judaism, or Buddhism, there are stories of or about that religion that believers told. Some of them are truly remarkable, but are either of the remarkable stories truly believable? Millions of people on either side believe their stories to be true.

Personally speaking I'm not so sure about any of them. Before Abraham, the father of the Jewish faith came along many people worshiped many different gods and idols. I want to make it clear that I am not anti-religion or an atheist; it's just that I'm still searching for the truth at this time in my life. I'm smart enough to know that there is something or some force out there that is much more powerful and greater than myself that created this Big Ball that we call Earth and everything on it.

But with that being said, there is still something I have to add. For all the millions of believers in the Adam and Eve account, I must say that there are a couple of issues that need to be addressed because there is the big Blue Whale in the room. I will elaborate on those issues in an upcoming Act of these writings in hopes of shedding clarity for my readers. So please bear with me on this.

Now according to Darwin's theory and other scientists, paleontologists, and anthropologists, all of them believe mankind evolved on this Earth by way of natural selection. This means they all seem to dismiss the Adam and Eve scenario. These brilliant minds say that all life evolved from microscopic organisms from the vast oceans and seas covering three-quarters of the Earth's surface. They base their theory on ancient fossils they have discovered all around the planet dating back millions of years.

The oldest non-human fossil, a giant prehistoric sea-dwelling creature, the Stegosaurus, was uncovered in Kansas in 1991 by the palynologist Donald Carl Johansson. Carbon dating determined the age of that magnificent specimen to be well over 84 million years old. As remarkable of discovery as this was, there are two other discoveries that I feel superseded it when it comes to focusing on the human race.

One of the most significant Hominid fossils was uncovered in 1994 by paleoanthropologist Tim White and his team of scientists in Awash, Ethiopia. What they found was a female skeleton that after a careful study determined that she was well over 4.4 million years old. They decided to name her Ardi, short for Ardipithecus and was determined to be the oldest human ancestor ever found. Prior to Ardi another team of scientists led by Johanson made history in 1974 when they uncovered the skeletal remains of a female Australopithecus, another human-like species. She was also found in Ethiopia and was determined to be 3.2 million years old. They named her Lucy. These two discoveries are significant because they give scientists worldwide more credence to their theory of evolution. This means the scientific community doesn't believe in the religious story of Adam and Eve. To them, it is just that: a beautiful story.

Act-3: The Human Race

Now that the two arguments of how the human race came to be have been discussed allow me to give you a theoretical assessment of both views. My assessment aims to observe and articulate our evolutionary process, if at all possible.

Talking about the evolution theory first, let's say for a moment that we did evolve from the likes of Ardi and Lucy over millions of years. This means that after millions of years of sleeping in trees like our ancestors such as chimpanzees and apes, we evolved into the Neanderthals.

After moving out of the trees we sought shelter in the mountains and caves because it provided more protection and safety from environmental elements and predators. That would make it one of the first intelligent things we, as Neanderthals or Homo Sapiens figured out.

Now, we don't know which gender came up with the idea to move out of the trees and into the caves. But I would put my money on the female. In any case we know we became cave dwellers for millions of years. We know this because of the works of scientists, anatomists, emeritus, and theorists such as Raymond Dart and C.K. "Bob" Brain, who explored and studied caves in the South African Limestone Caves. These caves are located less than 200 miles from Johannesburg in a region known as "The Cradle Of Mankind." These men uncovered fossils and bones from at least four hominid species dating as far back as 1.8 million years ago.

Another point that needs to be addressed is as confusing as it is important because this is by no means a matter of skin color. It is an all-inclusive thing; no nationality is exempt. If we are to conclude that mankind evolved from the continent of Africa the question then becomes, how did these Neanderthals make their way from The Cradle in Africa all the way to Central Europe and the La Ferrassie Cave in France?

That is where in 1909 scientists Denis Peyromy and Louis Capitan uncovered what seems to be a family of eight Homo Neanderthalensis that were buried, by design, near the La Ferrassie Cave. This discovery suggests that the inhabitants cared for each other, but strangely in some of the caves there were signs of cannibalism as well.

This makes the follow-up question even more interesting: How and when did the Neanderthal skeletons uncovered in 1957 by another team of scientists in the Shanidar Cave of Iraq, make their way to Western Asia over 45,000 years ago?

That discovery was to this day, the largest one regarding Neanderthals throughout history with ten individuals, including adults and children. On further examination it was determined that one of the adults had met his demise by way of a stab wound. This means somebody may have gotten away with murder back then suggesting that violence was probably the normal way of life. In those days the male species had to be strong, cunning, brutal, and carry a huge stick to survive. Due to such behavior the male species had no problem taking whatever he wanted, even the female he wanted.

This led the scientists to conclude that over the course of thousands of years Homo Sapiens and/or Neanderthals had to have migrated from Africa to Europe. That is the reason why fossils and skeletons were uncovered in caves in all three places: LimeStone Cave in Africa, Shanidar Cave in Iraq, and La Ferrassie Cave in France.

We know that for thousands of years these species roamed the world in some of the harshest climates and only the fittest of either species endured. But there came a time when some species like the Neanderthals became extinct, or was their trace simply lost in time? It is highly possible that these brutal, notorious, and cannibalistic beings evolved into what scientists now call the modern human.

This theory leaves no doubt that we are the results of evolution, just as the evolution chart suggests.

Act-4: The Garden of Eden

Now, let us discuss the theosophical interpretation of God Almighty. He was the one who decided to create a species in His likeness, with Adam and Eve being the first two of their kind. We know where He decided to place these two species and that was said to be in The Garden of Eden. And how do we know this? Because the Bible tells us so.

But what the Bible does not tell us is just when or what year God placed Adam and Eve in that Garden. Why? I don't know the answer to that question, nor do I believe the scribes of the Bible know the answer either. Even scientists can't agree on a time, and some believed it might have been 80,000 years ago until other scientists uncovered fossilized human remains that dated as far back as 150,000 years ago.

Ironically those numbers overlap with some of the same numbers that suggest the Neanderthals may have become extinct, which means this question will remain a historical mystery. With this being said it now brings up a whole new set of questions. As I alluded to earlier there is this big Blue Whale in the room.

We know Adam and Eve were the first two humans set on Earth if we are to believe in the Bible's account of the beginning of man and woman. We also know that together they brought three children, two males, and a female into this world. Again, we know this because the Bible told us so. The two male offspring were Cain and Abel. Life continued swimmingly except for a few hick-ups between brothers, which is natural. It wasn't until the

13

third offspring of Adam & Eve, Awan, a beautiful little girl was born and came into maturity that things seemed to have gone awry.

Somewhere in the timeline of the three siblings growing up either Cain or Awan fell to temptation, much like their mother, Eve when it came to the "Apple Bite." But the temptation that Cain and Awan fell into was not the biting of an apple, nor was it a tree-bearing fruit. But Cain's temptation resembled that of another fruit of sorts (if you get my drift). Over time these siblings became attracted to one another to the point that they crossed the line into what has to be the first act of incest that is rarely talked about.

Why?

Then again maybe it wasn't a consensual act in the beginning at all. After all, Cain showed how violent he could be when he chose to murder his own brother, Abel. It says in the Bible that Awan was Cain's wife. My question is, who married them? Who's to say that Cain didn't just take her by knocking on her head, which later became a common act for thousands of years? After he took her, if indeed that is what he did, he just called her his wife. Surely, God didn't sanction that incestual marriage.

The violent act that Cain perpetrated against his brother Abel and the brother-sister act that Cain and Awan were involved in had to be, if not heartbreaking, at least a bit disappointing to God. This meant that God had to realize that the species he put on Earth in His image to replace the dinosaurs were also flawed and violent.

It is said that God makes no mistakes which may be true because Adam, Eve, Caine, and Awan were all members of the first family that committed the sins, not He.

The question that comes to mind is, did God not, after placing Adam and Eve in the Garden place others (unrelated) in areas near the Garden to ensure that the act of incest would be minimized? If He didn't place others in close proximity that means there had to be continuous acts of incest occurring throughout the years. This factor is the big Blue Whale in the room.

The unintentional consequences of allowing something as serious as incest to go unchecked would devastate the population in so many ways, none of which would enhance or improve the race for years to come, if ever. Studies have been performed in England, Michigan, and Czechoslovakia on live-born children produced as a result of incest. In one study scientists followed over 150 such children from birth and nearly half of them were found to have recessive disorders.

The disorders included adiposogenital syndrome, homocystinuria, congenital ichthyosis, as well as a high rate of retardation. The other studies that were performed included 31 children, 19 born to brother-sister and 12 born to father-daughter, and out of those only a third were classified as being normal, and the other two-thirds were found to have similar disorders as the children in the first study.

Although these studies took place within the last century the behavior of incest was started shortly after the beginning of mankind with devastating results. Such acts would have manifested themselves in the surrounding area of the Garden thousands of years ago. It would have profoundly affected the development of the human brain to this very day. God created man in His physical image and I assume he planned to do it to perfection, but it didn't turn out to be so.

The brain is the most complicated organ and/or muscle in the human body, yet it is also the most fragile. Armed with this knowledge, reasonable and educated people such as you and I could only conclude that a percentage of the population to this day are among those that were not considered to be normal and are living all around us - a frightening but reasonable thought.

This is a possible reality. Your belief in the chronicles of Adam, Eve, Caine, Abel, and Awan matters very little.

Act-5: Cradle of Civilization

The believers of evolution would argue that the cradle of civilization, as well as the rest of the hominids, appeared in South Africa, not the Garden of Eden or the surrounding areas, Mesopotamia, present day (Iraq and Iran). Their theory is based on findings from excavations going back as far as 200,000 years.

There are a few other regions that also claim to be the cradle of civilization, including Egypt, Pakistan, and Afghanistan. We have to be clear about just what The Cradle of Civilization really means. It simply means it is the start of the era when the early human species upgraded their living standards by moving into caves and branched out from there to building huts, houses, and then communities.

Thousands of years before the transition from trees to caves, the jungles were wild and dangerous for all because cannibalism and incest were the norm throughout the jungles. Chimpanzees were among the most feared primates in the jungle because they would roam the grounds in packs and hunt for their meals, much like hyenas and lions do in the plains of Africa. What separated the chimpanzees from the other predators was their prey of choice. Their prey was mostly other monkeys, and to this day, they still hunt in the same fashion as their ancestors. If one were to believe in Darwin's theory, one would have to conclude that Homo Sapiens, Neanderthals, and Humans had to have inherited the violent, murderous, incestuous, and cannibalistic behaviors of their ancestors, i.e., the chimpanzee.

Whatever theory one chooses to believe in whether it be the Bible's Adam and Eve or Darwin's theory of evolution, the fact remains that man since the beginning has displayed the propensity to do harm and even kill his fellow man and or woman.

Now I wouldn't think that when God decided to create man in His own image He couldn't have foreseen that Adam's and Eve's sons would become so combative that one would want to kill the other, or could He? People who believe in God and that God created man also believe He created all living things, past and present, which takes us back to His early creations. They include the carnivorous dinosaurs and the Homotherium (better known as the saber-tooth tiger-cat), the giant sea creatures such as the Mosasaurus and the Megalodon, the largest shark that ever lived, plus other jungle-dwelling predators as well.

The brains he put into the heads of those creatures were programmed to kill and devour their prey to survive, which meant a major portion of their brain was simply the kill zone. When God decided to step up His game and create a less violent creature such as man, He had to have understood that the brain He put into the earlier creatures that made them so dangerous could not work for the human brain.

This means that He Too had to redesign the brain for humans, i.e., Adam and Eve. The brain would have to be a less violent design for the more civil and docile earthlings who were to live on His Earth peacefully going forward. The human brain is so much more complicated than that of the wild and dangerous creatures that God once had roaming the Earth hundreds of millions of years ago. During the redesigning of the human brain

God must have inadvertently integrated a variant of the Gene called the RRKD-G (Rage-Ravage-Kill-Devour-Gene), which was the one He placed in the carnivore's brains millions of years ago.

The variant Gene that He placed in the human brain was RRKD-G (Rage-Rape-Kill-Destroy-Gene), which was also flawed. This design flaw in the human brain didn't take long to reveal itself, the proof of that came to pass when Cain took it upon himself to stone his brother Abel to death. The scary thing about that flaw is that it is inheritable from father to son and daughter, to a lesser degree. Yet the Gene remains dormant in 95% of the human race. This has been happening for generations, and Cain, if he lived as long as noted, some 700 plus years, the many offspring he fathered inherited the Gene and they too passed it on to their children throughout the world for centuries to come.

Act-6: Mother Nature

The theory of evolution states that dinosaurs and humans evolved from microscopic organisms from the seas and or oceans of the world. This theory is just as, if not more extraordinary as some of the events that God is said to have performed throughout the Bible. Events such as creating Eve from the rib of Adam, assisting Moses in the parting of the Red Sea, and giving his son Jesus the power to turn water into wine and rise from the dead, only to name a few.

Evolution theorists state that the giant creatures such as the T-Rex and Velociraptor that roamed the earth millions of years ago grew and evolved from tiny reptiles such as geckos and lizards. They also say that the huge killer sharks evolved from the likes of minnows and tadpoles. So if evolution, also known as Mother Nature, is responsible for the carnivore dinosaurs and the giant killer sharks that means that she also decided to evolve us, the human race, from chimpanzees millions of years later.

This also means that she is magnificent in her own right. But she, too, failed to alter that RRKD-Gene (Rage-Ravage-Kill-Devour-Gene) from the brain she placed in her dinosaurs and other prehistoric predators. That would mean that she placed a similar variant in the chimpanzee which evolved into the human brain. This accounts for why the chimpanzee, our closest ancestor out of all of the other primates, guerrillas, baboons, and monkeys, are the only ones that hunt, kill, and devour their own kind even to this day. These primates, our closest ancestors, not only engage in cannibalism but also have a ferocious appetite for promiscuous sex and participate in incest between brother and sister, son and mother, father and daughter, or whoever is there at the time. Through the many millennia of evolution from chimpanzees to Homo Erectus and then to Homo Sapiens, although the brains are larger and the Rage-Ravage-Kill-Devour-Gene was replaced with the Rage-Rape-Kill-Destroy-Gene, it remains in the brains of Homo Sapiens to this day.

The fact of the matter is that whichever belief or religion one chooses to honor they have to realize that man, whether created by Mother Nature or God Almighty, has persevered through the difficult struggles of life. It has taken hundreds of thousands of years for man to even learn how to live side-by-side with his neighbor in peace.

As the population exploded on the continent of Africa, the migrations continued to spread throughout all the countries, forming different tribes and kingdoms. Unfortunately, man is not a perfect being. The evidence is clear: we as people today are products of our past, our ancestors, and we all carry, believe it or not, the (RRKD-G).

There is no way to sugarcoat the fact that man, by nature, is a violent species and has displayed it throughout history. A lot of the acts committed by men to their fellow men and women were cruel and horrendous. It could be justified by saying that man had to be violent in order to survive, but that would be too easy of a way out, and only half-true.

Act-7: Pharaohs, Kings, & Queens

As the great migration continued northward the Kingdoms expanded and they were ran by kings and pharaohs such as Djoser III (2686-2648 B.C.) and Tutankhamun (1332-1323 B.C.) in North Africa or Egypt over the millennia.

Pharaoh Djoser III

Born in 2670 B.C., Djoser III grew up and came to be the 2nd King of the 3rd Dynasty of Ancient Egypt in a similar way as his father, King Khasekhemwy, and his mother, Queen Nimaathap, both of whom were said to have been two of the worst tyrants of that time. The path of Djoser III to infamy began early on as a teenager when his parents chose him over his older brother to take over the throne. The reason was that they thought his brother was too weak to lead.

Less than six years later both parents of Djoser III died. This meant that he took his place as Pharaoh of the 3rd Dynasty. He Too continued on the same path that his father and mother once embarked on; Djoser III inherited not only the throne from his parents, but He Too inherited their foul double dose of the RRKD-G. This meant that Egypt was in for another six years of brutal leadership. While attempting to follow in his father's footsteps Djoser III quickly realized that it was easier said than actually accomplishing such a task. The brutality and mistreatment of the people of Egypt was the easy part, coupled with his habits of womanizing, drinking, and partying, which seemed to be second nature to King Djoser III.

During those years He Too managed to acquire over 80 concubines, fathering over 50 children between them. King Djoser lll was breeding like a Jack Rabbit! In his spare time when he was not sewing his Royal Oats Djoser lll would focus on doing his business, and He Too would find time to do Egypt's business as well. Djoser lll was a man of vision and fancied himself as an architect of multiple things. In order to prove to himself and his people that he could create, Djoser lll moved to Memphis along with his trusted vizier, Imhotep, so that they could start building what is now his famous Step Pyramid. The site Djoser lll chose for the building of his Great Pyramid and necropolis was in Saqqara, not far from the capital of Egypt, Memphis.

To build his magnificent pyramid, Djoser lll ordered thousands of his slaves to begin clearing the grounds for the foundation of the first pyramid of its kind in ancient Egypt. He Too needed to finance this major undertaking, so Djoser lll sent his soldiers on missions to Sinai to pillage it, taking and mining all of its valuables and enslaving all of the nomadic people along the way.

What Djoser lll achieved was nothing short of a miracle during that time period, or even by today's standards and technology. This is simply because those 3 or 4-ton stones cannot be placed today as precisely as they were placed when that pyramid was built. It would be impossible to recreate such a feat! And even if one tried to replicate it, the physical manpower and secrets it took to build and create such a magnificent landmark have been lost over time.

Djoser lll was one of the most powerful, if not the most powerful, Pharaohs ever to have ruled Egypt. While his father and mother ruled Djoser III was taking notes and making plans to take the leadership of his parents to another level. It was as though a vision came to him and he set out to bring it to completion. It's also possible that as a child Djoser III came across a colony of army ants, studied it, and mastered the workings of the ants in his mind. Learning what he could from studying the army of ants and when he came into power, Djoser III would mimic the same discipline and power over his huge army as did the Queen Ant displayed with her army.

Okay, maybe it is a bit far out there to think army ants influenced Djoser III to control his people, but he was a brutal and selfish tyrant. Another theory about how Djoser III had his slaves build that magnificent pyramid seems even more far-fetched, like outer space far-fetched!

There are conspiracy theorists who believe there were, and still are, beings from another space in the vast galaxy above. These theorists, too, believe that aliens first came to Earth in 2666 B.C. to search for minerals such as silver, platinum, and gold that they needed to survive on their planet. The technology and expertise that they brought here to excavate and mine for those minerals they needed was the same that they used to assist Djoser III and his slaves in the construction of what is believed to be the first pyramid built in Egypt.

Some theorists also contend that the extraterrestrials remained here on Earth until 2550 B.C. when they returned to their faraway planet, but not before assisting Pharaoh Khufu in the construction of his Great Pyramids of Giza and stripping this planet of 50% of its valuable minerals.

Now, you can't get any further out than that. To this day it is still a mystery how these Pharaohs erected all of those magnificent pyramids in Egypt.

Hatshepsut

The most ironic fact about such dictators is that one of the most feared and ruthless ones of all time just so happened to be a woman. In fact, there were three such brutal and feared female pharaohs. The first one that comes to mind is Hatshepsut, who ruled with an iron fist back in the 18th Dynasty (1503-1482 B.C). She held not one, not two, but three titles: one as Pharaoh, then as King, then the other as Queen. To solidify her place in the Kingdom she ripped a page out of history and ended up marrying her half-brother, Thutmosis II, her father's son, Thutmosis I.

She, Hatshepsut, committed incest much like, though not exactly, Caine did by marrying his sister, Awan. Hatshepsut was not only the first leader in history to hold three titles, but was also the first woman in history to adopt the fashion trend of Cross Dressing. Not only did she don the nest of women's garments, but she also dressed in the traditional King and Royal attire as well. Such attire included but was not limited to, wearing the fashionable Egypt King's beard when necessary. The marriage between Hatshepsut and her half-brother was in name only, just for her to legitimize her status as Queen. She satisfied her womanly needs by demanding her sexual needs be met and performed by her cabinet ministers or the house slaves. When she desired a stud he would be summoned and there would be dire consequences if he were to refuse her sexual advances. Hatshepsut was the only female Pharaoh of Egypt who was the most feared and brutal one because she inherited one of the worst variants of the RRKD-G from her father. She paved the way for a couple of other well-known female pharaohs, such as Nefertiti, born in 1370 B.C., and Cleopatra, who was born in 69 B.C., and both were tyrants in their own right.

Nefertiti

Nefertiti, at first, was not a Pharaoh but she married Pharaoh Akhenaten at the age of 15 years old and became the powerful Queen and his Wife. Together they ruled from 1353 to 1336 B.C., but Akhenaten was considered Egypt's worst Pharaoh ever - a criminal to the people.

She became a Pharaoh only after the death of her husband and from early on ruled much more harshly than her husband. They both carried a dark strain of the RRKD-G, and she was also considered to be and earned the name of, Ice Queen. It wasn't until some years later that some say Nefertiti became a more subdued and compassionate leader once she settled into power. However, she had the belief that the only God she would worship was the Sun God (Aten) and that the Sun was the only God worthy of Egypt's loyalty, but she still led supremely.

Nefertiti never let the fact that she lost one eye prevent her from becoming and remaining a powerful force throughout her reign. She was the first and only Pharaoh in history to ever lead an empire with one eye.

Moreover, she was in fact the first woman in history to publicly state that she believed in and advocated for Women's Rights and expressed that women should strive to be independent of their men and seek power over their own destinies. I don't know why she has not yet received any recognition for being a proto-feminist; she so deserves to be the Poster Woman for the feminist organization of today!

Pharaoh Tutankhamun

In 1353, in ancient Egypt, a man with the names of Akhenaten and Amenhotep IV was crowned as a Pharaoh in the capital, Memphis. During his reign, Amenhotep IV was said to have been a ruthless tyrant and cared nothing about what would happen to cities and states surrounding Egypt's Asiatic Empire. When asked by Rib-Hadda, one of Amenhotep IV's vassals and King of Byblos to send some troops to help him fight off invaders from Hittites, Amenhotep IV refused to do so. Even after over 50 letters begging him for help, he never sent the help that was needed.

Amenhotep IV was a cruel Pharaoh who was only concerned about leaving a legacy of wealth for his son, who was yet to be conceived. Amenhotep IV was not only a cruel Pharaoh; He Too was a womanizer in that he had at least three wives and queens and several concubines. From all of them he fathered 6 to 7 children, all of them girls. He wanted to have a son so badly that he didn't care who his mother would be and began having sex with a few of his own daughters. His dark strain of the RRKD-G manifested itself in this way. Finally in 1341 B.C., one of his women (historians are not sure which one) gave him a baby boy. Amenhotep IV named his son Tutankhamun and proudly called him "King Tut" for short. Unfortunately he was born with numerous physical and mental disabilities and needed a cane to walk around because he had a bone necrosis condition. Tutankhamun was only 9 or 10 years old when he took the throne and became the Pharaoh of Egypt. Shortly after that his mental disabilities began to surface, those being several strains of malaria and scoliosis, which some historians attribute to incest. It has been said that his mother was actually one of his older sisters, while other historians believe that his mother might have been Queen Nefertiti.

King Tut was said to have married his half-sister. They tried to have children of their own but failed twice, once by miscarriage and the other time by their baby girl dying a few months after birth. Again, some say incest was the cause of these deaths.

King Tut not only inherited the throne from his father, He Too inherited his father's dark strain of the RRKD-G, along with his greed and the habit of womanizing. He ruled as Pharaoh only for a short time because he died at the early age of 20 years old, but he managed to accumulate wealth well beyond his dreams during that time.

Cleopatra

Cleopatra inherited the throne of Egypt from her father, Ptolemy XII (Auletes), who was a descendant of Ptolemy I Soter, who happened to have been one of Alexander the Great's generals. Cleopatra was only 18 years old when her father Auletes died, leaving her as heir in 51 B.C. alongside her younger 10-year-old brother. Cleopatra inherited not only the throne but also the dark strain of the RRKD-G from her father who was a brutal tyrant of Egypt. When she made up her mind and wanted something done to elevate her position nothing could stop her. When she felt the need to put her son in power she found it necessary to have her half-brother, whom she married not once but twice, killed to make way for her son to become King.

As ruthless and powerful as Cleopatra was, her plot to have her blood brother Ptolemy III killed failed. Once Ptolemy III got wind of her plan he wanted her head on a platter. So she had to escape Egypt, and after roaming for a few months ended up in Syria. Cleopatra remained in Syria for a little more than a year until she got word that Julius Caesar was in Alexandria. She then decided to make her way back to Egypt to garner his support.

Caesar welcomed her for a couple of reasons; first he needed to repay the debts that her father Auletes owed to Rome, and *second,* he admired her and wanted to make her Queen of Egypt again.

Caesar first called on his reinforcements and they ran her brother Ptolemy III off the throne and out of Alexandria. It was said that he drowned in the Nile River while trying to escape toward freedom. Soon after that Cleopatra had her army round up all of Ptolemy III's loyalists and executed them.

Thanks to Caesar Cleopatra regained her rightful place on the throne of Egypt and brought her 13-year-old younger brother as well. Caesar and Cleopatra remained together in Egypt for a while, and they too, had a son and for some strange reason they also named him Ptolemy. Cleopatra's reign as queen was full of tragedy and sorrow which just added to her already tyrant ways.

Caesar returned to Rome and a year or two later in March 44 B.C., he was assassinated so Cleopatra went back to Egypt soon after. Not long after she returned her brother Ptolemy XIV was killed leaving her and her young son on the throne. A short time later Cleopatra partnered with one of Caesar's close friends Mark Antony, and they went to war together and defeated the two men who had assassinated Caesar: Brutus and Cassius.

In 40 B.C., Antony and Cleopatra became *one* and she bore him a set of twins. Then in 36 B. C. they had another child. In September of 31 B.C. Antony and Cleopatra were defeated by the Octavian in the Battle of Actium after which Cleopatra fled back to Egypt ahead of Antony.

Antony was a brutal tyrant and He Too was inflicted with a dark strain of RRKD-G, but he was deeply in love with Cleopatra. So when he heard rumors that she had committed suicide he fell on his sword killing himself. The sad thing about that is that the rumors were not true; she was alive and well in Alexandria. Once Cleopatra heard about Antony's death and why he killed himself she had her soldiers hunt down and kill those who spread the rumor of her death. After she buried Antony she committed suicide and was buried right next to her true love—Mark Antony. She was only 39 years old when she died.

Moving Forward

As a result of migrating the population reached not only northern and eastern Africa, but over a long period of time people also ventured into Asia and European Russia. The migration continued north to East Europe. As the population continued to grow people in different areas decided to elect Dictators, Kings, and Queens. During the same time the migration continued to northeast Russia, crossing over Alaska, then going south to Canada, and finally down to what is now the United States. Over time this is where people became Prime Ministers and Presidents. It seems as though the further north and east men traveled to the other continents such as Asia and Europe the lighter their complexions became, which was no doubt due to the climate differences in which they lived.

But what didn't change was the fact that they all carried with them the RRKD-G to those various countries and continents. It remained in their brains wherever they decided to settle. It is truly astonishing how the modern world developed and how the different nationalities spread and went their separate ways. Through the ages they all seemed to develop different languages and beliefs on how countries and nations should be run. There were leaders and followers and in most cases the leaders had absolute power and control over the population. This too meant that the leaders determined who lived and who died and even who they could take to their bed.

Act-8: Conquerors and Tyrants

The population was continuing to explode in other parts of the globe and as a result there were men in those areas who felt the need to take control and lead the masses. The direction that they thought was fitting included unity and obedience at all costs and for that, they took their power by brutality and force.

Liu Bang

There was one such person who lived in one of China's poorest towns, Pei County. He was born in about 250 B.C. and given the name Liu Bang. Growing up in that ghetto town watching his mother and father struggle to provide for him and his family he decided that he had to do something different. Once Bang came of age He Too became eligible with no education to land a job. The job he landed was of an enforcement officer in the town he had grown up in. He ran it with brute force as if the town was his own. This young man had his sights on becoming a leader in his country while growing up during the Qin Dynasty. He studied and learned about the brutality that took place by the leader of the said dynasty. During the building of the Great Wall Bang was witness to how many millions of people it took to build it and how many died, with no mercy as they were building it.

What Qin Shi Huang didn't know was that when he appointed Bang to the position of enforcement officer for that sector of China, is that he set in motion the events that would lead to Bang becoming the next Emperor of the whole of China. Bang watched and took meticulous notes while working under and for the Qin Dynasty. During this time Bang realized that He Too was capable of great brutality without remorse or pity for the people under his rule. Bang's coalescence began in the sector of his home town then he spread his power throughout the country pillaging, raping, and killing anyone who opposed him. Bang had developed this insatiable appetite for power and he was determined to achieve absolute control over the country. Bang's RRKD-G was revealing itself and although Qin Shi Huang himself was a brutal tyrant with a high degree of the RRKD-G, Bang's degree of the Gene was a deadlier strain and could not be abated. Bang and his loyal followers, the majority of whom came from the poor sector where he was raised and many others rebelled against the Qin Empire.

Shortly afterward Qin was killed which opened the door wider for Bang as he marched toward his goal of becoming the leader of all of China. After defeating several rival armies he established his dominance in the country and a short time after he saw a clear path to toppling the Qin Empire around 202 B.C. Once Bang stepped into the new position he had brutally fought for – Emperor, he felt it was time to change his name because to him Liu Bang was too ghetto a name for such a position. He Too thought the title of Emperor alone was not enough so he decided to change his name to one that was more fitting of his achievements. He chose the name Han Gaozu.

Emperor Han Gaozu's long and violent journey began as a poor boy but his drive and desire to be someone other than a commoner and his willingness to take out his rage on anyone, to kill and destroy anyone that got in his way paid off for him. Gaozu's determination landed him at the top with power and riches well beyond his greedy imagination. After settling into his new role as Emperor Gaozu he began making drastic changes in the way China had been run under the previous leadership. He made it clear that he, and only he, had complete and absolute power over all of China.

It didn't take long before Han felt the need to create his very own dynasty and did exactly that in 206 B.C. naming it, The Han Dynasty which went on to become what they called, The Golden Age in China. This man formerly known as Liu Bang with no formal education rose through the ranks unmercifully and led his country to untold wealth and prosperity. He Too created a dynasty that lasted 400 years, the longest in China's history.

Although Han conquered and took his way to prominence and power in doing so, he lifted and led the country of China into becoming a major World power. Han's rise to power—from being born in dire poverty to becoming the leader of one of the most populated countries in the world—was nothing short of miraculous. It is considered to be the most spectacular rise from rags to riches story ever told in China, and arguably in the world.

Alexander the Great

In another time and another part of the world in the year 359 B.C. there lived a king, King Philip II, who was King of Macedon in northern Greece. Unlike Liu Bang who had to use his primitive RRKD-G to rise from nothing to get to the top of his game, King Philip II was grandfathered into power when his uncle was killed in war. Philip then took over the Macedon Dynasty from 359 until 336 B.C. and He Too was just as brutal and dangerous as his uncle before him. They both had a potent active RRKD-G. So in the natural order of things King Philip passed his RRKD-G onto his son. Alexander who would become widely known as Alexander the Great.

King Philip was assassinated in late 336 B.C. by one of his bodyguards which opened the door for his son Alexander to take over the throne and carry out the ambitions of his father. One of his father's ambitions was to conquer the Persian Empire. So several years before King Philip was killed he made sure that he educated Alexander in a way that would prepare him to take over as King when the time came. Alexander was taught by the best horseman how to ride and train horses, and He Too was educated and taught to read and write by top scholars of the times. One such scholar went by the name of Aristotle.

It is said that Alexander was this mild-mannered young man who had no desire to become the leader of his people because his father's footsteps were so large and difficult to fill.

Once Alexander realized that the bodyguard who betrayed and killed his father was a man he knew and admired, it was too much for him to bear. It was then that the RRKD-G that he had inherited from his father which had been lying dormant during his adolescent years activated all of a sudden. By some accounts it was Alexander himself who took revenge against the bodyguard, the murderer of his father by beheading him in front of thousands of onlookers.

The murder of his father unleashed a lot of anger and rage in him that continued for many years to come and he took it out on all of those who stood in his way. His first personal act of revenge was just the beginning of the rampage that he would take out on his enemies for years to come. His next act was to assemble an army of like-minded loyal followers who would do his bidding in war and show no mercy on his enemies. He Too with his army, went on to brutally conquer the Achaemenid (Persian Empire) and in doing so gave his army the green light to rape and pillage throughout the country and beyond. It is truly astounding how one man can ignite the RRKD-G that lay dormant in others by just displaying his own rage and anger, but this was more common than one realizes. In wars throughout history for instance, the raping and taking of women and girls by hundreds if not thousands of warriors led by their leader was accepted behavior.

After his success in the Achaemenid Alexander went on to continue his war campaign in nearby Asia Minor, Egypt, and Syria. He Too attempted to invade India but was met with less success. That invasion didn't happen because India was not having it. They were armed and ready for whatever Alexander had planned. In fact, India was armed in such a way that had not been seen in any of the aforementioned invasions, and the outcome was absolute.

Alexander's army charged their way into the jungles of India only to be met with not just an army of men but also an army of full-grown angry elephants, over 50 strong with horns up to 6 feet long.

I don't know if that was Alexander's first defeat but it was surely his worst. Those Indians kicked and sent his ass back home. There would be no young Indian women raped, no Indian treasures looted, nor would there be any Indian concubines for Alexander or his soldiers to take, not in India!

He succeeded in all the rest of his invasions, not necessarily in that order but with the same rage and brutality. Alexander's accomplishments included invading, conquering, pillaging, and raping all of the countries mentioned above with the exception of India, and for that reason he earned himself the title of Alexander the Great.

Hannibal

In a faraway land in Northeastern Africa in the year 247 B.C., a future brutal conquer was born. His name was Hamilcar Barca. Little is known about his upbringing while living in Carthage or who his father was, but it is a fact that his father passed on a raw variant of the RRKD-G to him. Barca grew up to become an intelligent young warrior for the Carthaginian military and wasted no time in earning the rank of General and Statesman.

He Too was tagged with the word *Great* in his name as a Great Carthaginian General for his accomplishments in the 1st Punic War. His claims to fame included but were not limited to, ravaging, pillaging, and raping during his attacks on the coastline of Italy. His brutal attacks stretched from Lucania, Bruttium, and as far north as Cumae.

One could argue that his biggest accomplishment was fathering his son whom he named Hannibal. Barca took his child with him when he was ten years old to Spain in 237 B.C. during one of his most brutal campaigns there.

Unfortunately after several years Hamilcar Barca died during that said campaign by drowning in a river near a place called Helice in the year 229 B.C. His death came as a futile attempt to evade capture by the Celtiberian army ending his reign of terror in that region. The untimely death of Barca left his son Hannibal to carry out what his father had started. For nine years Hannibal watched with admiration how his father ran his war campaign and he promised his father that he would carry out his wish to invade and overthrow the mighty Roman empire.

The absence of his father did nothing to diminish Hannibal's desire to go forward with his said promise even though the odds of success were astronomical. The RRKD-G that he inherited from his father was so intense that he thought he could build a large enough army after ravaging Spain to cross the mighty Alps. He figured that by doing that, he would then have a clear path to Rome where he could then conquer it.

Remarkably, Hannibal did just that. He formed an army of over 30 thousand strong and prepared them for the 1500 plus miles journey across the Alps into Italy. He was not only able to form a huge army of men but He Too took a page out of India's war chest and recruited close to 60 elephants and over 15,000 horses to join in for the journey.

It is said and argued by some scholars that it took Hannibal and his army only 20 or 30 days to cross over the mighty Alps to get to northern Italy. In any case the journey was bitter, cold, and harsh, which meant many soldiers died, and all but a few of the elephants died in the mountains as well. Once Hannibal and his not-so-merry men made their descent from the mountains they found themselves in a new country. The new country was Northern Italy and it was ripe for the pickings, and that is just what Hannibal instructed his men to begin doing. So they pillaged, raped, and killed.

The small northern town called Milan, in northern Italy, was founded in 600 B.C. and is to this day, still considered to be the wealthiest town in all of Italy.

Hannibal and his army wasted no time, and in less than three months the city of Milan was unrecognizable. After getting their fill of the city they moved south toward Bologna. Hannibal spent a year there and then went on to Naples where they began a 15-year war campaign, taking over and pillaging all cities in southern Italy. Although Hannibal was considered Rome's worst enemy and as greedy and violent as he was he could never put his hands on that Grand Prize that he swore to his father he would obtain.

As you recall just like how one of his earlier fellow conquerors, Alexander The Great, failed in his attempt to conquer India, Hannibal also failed to complete his main objective. He failed even after all the hard work of traveling over the Alps, taking and raping all of those women, pillaging, and killing countless Italian citizens. Hannibal spread fear and death throughout the cities of Italy but he still failed to get the elusive Prize—Rome. A hero he was not! Hannibal and Alexander were both takers. They took the land, they took valuables, they took lives, and they took women.

Attila The Hun

In a different time and place many years later there was an up-and-coming leader living in central Europe. He went by the name "Attila," better known as Attila the Hun. He Too rose to prominence and power after being raised in poverty with little or nothing to eat as a child. Hun's dire circumstances growing up fueled his desire to become a man of resources and power by any means possible. Hun's anger and disregard for others came from his father, Mundzuk, by way of birth inheriting a lethal strain of the RRKD-G.

It wasn't until 434 A.D. that Attila made a name for himself and earned his way by brute force, the title and the leadership of the tribes of the Huns and Alans in central and eastern Europe. Attila's bold leadership presence was such that he was able to assemble an army of what is said to have been close to a half million soldiers. These men were willing to follow him in his quest to declare war on towns, cities, and countries near and far. His foremost claim to fame was that he was considered to be the most brutal warlord in ancient world history - a reputation that preceded him wherever he went. Attila began his march toward what he thought was to be his world dominance by invading Gaul, present-day France, and all townships and cities along the way. After he and his huge army raped, pillaged and took over Gaul, HeToo set his sights on nearby northern Italy.

Long before Attila decided to invade other countries he and the Huns were already considered by many in Central and Eastern Europe and even as far away as Northern and Southern Italy to be barbarians. Attila did his best to live up to that negative description with pride and it is noted that he even killed his own brother so that he would remain the Emperor of The Huns.

Italy became aware of Attila's invasion of Gaul long before he crossed the border into North Italy but could do little to stop his mighty forces that were headed their way. Italy was at the mercy of Attila because it had no army large enough to fend off any aggression by such tyrants, plus they were a friendly and vulnerable nation.

In 452 A.D., Attila led his army through Northeastern Italy with the intent to make his way south, eventually getting to his main objective which was Rome. Crossing over the border Attila and his men invaded the city of Aquileia. Being true to his reputation they raped, pillaged, and killed anyone that stood in their way. The Attila army stayed in that city for a bit more than five months before moving southward to continue their rampage, leaving the city of Aquileia leveled to the ground.

The army had little mercy for any of the other cities as they marched south toward Rome and after two years Attila finally reached the cities surrounding Rome. Once they raped, plundered, and took control of said cities Attila decided it was a good time for him to take a break. He then gathered and packed up his portion of the loot that they had plundered, which was substantial along with a few concubines that He Too acquired from different cities in Italy and set on his way home.

Attila and a platoon of his army went back across the Danube to his palace where he planned to take care of some business and then celebrate his anniversary with one of his wives, Ildico. His plan then was to return to Italy and lead his army to the ultimate victory by taking Rome. But as fate would have it the mighty Attila the Hun would not step foot back onto Italian soil. The reason for that varies depending on what version of events one chooses to believe.

There is one account that states he was talked out of coming back to invade Rome by the diplomacy of Pope Leo. This would mean that his lifelong acts as a barbarian, rapist, and mass killer just so happened to end one day after listening to a Pope's plea. Are we to believe that Attila the Hun just all of a sudden had a

"Come-to-Jesus" moment and decided not to return to Italy and take Rome and all of its treasures?

And then there was a second reason which said that Attila didn't return to Italy to invade Rome because the then Eastern Emperor of Rome, Marcian, made sure that Attila was never able to get back to Italy by ending his life. How? We don't exactly know.

The third and not-so-fitting thing being said about the warrior and Emperor was that when Attila went back to his palace to celebrate his unfinished victory in Italy as well as his anniversary he just pretty much overindulged. As a consequence of his heavy partying on the second or third day Attila had such a heavy nosebleed that he couldn't control it and drowned in his own blood (Wow! Did they have cocaine back then?).

Whichever account one decides to believe the results are the same. He Too failed to reach his main objective after all the raping, pillaging, taking, and killing. Atila was never able to make Rome his own.

Genghis Khan

In the year 1162 A.D. in a nation bordered by China and Russia called Mongolia, there lived a man by the name of Yesugei. He fathered a son and named him Temujin. Temujin was born into a Royal Clan and lived very well for the first nine years of his life, that is, until his father was poisoned and died. Temujin was then held captive and lived poorly for years under the very people who were responsible for his father's death. What those people didn't know was that the RRKD-G that Temujin inherited from his father was a very potent strain. Nor did they have a clue as to what the depths of the repercussions of their actions against Temujin and his father would be.

Once he became a teenager Temujin figured out a way to escape from his terrible living conditions and that meant He Too had to kill his own brother to do so. After he was able to get far enough away from his captors he settled down in a small town and at the age of 19 changed his name to Genghis Khan. Khan then began putting together his loyal followers that would, in a few years, grow into an army of thousands.

Khan then set out to conquer nearby regions starting with the clan that poisoned his father and enslaved him, razing the region and taking no mercy out on asny of the inhabitants in said region.

After tasting the blood of revenge Genghis Khan made up his mind that he needed much more of everything which meant setting his sights on the vast territories surrounding Mongolia. As the years went by Genghis's army grew in size as did his desire to obtain wealth and power and he gained both by invading and pillaging towns and cities for as far as the eye could see. He felt entitled and he would not let anything or anyone prevent him from achieving his goal which was to be the most feared and powerful Emperor of all time.

By the age of 35 Genghis became just the one mentioned above. He ruled over one of the largest Empires in history. His invasions were not just restricted to the regions of Mongolia; they had also reached as far away as Central Asia and parts of China, expanding to the Caspian Sea. Genghis Khan took any and everything he wanted on his way to the top, especially women. At the top of his game Genghis had five wives, and it is said that He Too had upwards of an astounding and unbelievable 200 concubines on his roll-a-deck. Now if this is true the people who believed Genghis had 205 women would have no issue in believing that He Too fathered at least one child by no less than 100 of those women. This means that Genghis Khan had 100 offspring throughout a large region of Asia, ranging from the Pacific Ocean to the Caspian Sea.

That also means that not only did those offspring have his *Y* chromosomal lineage but they also had his deadly strain of the RRKD-G as well. Historians calculate that Genghis has contributed to the population as only one other man has in history accounting for approximately 0.5% of men that carry the Y chromosome which would today be north of 15 million of them. Many of his distant grand, great-great, grandsons are still roaming around the world today, not even knowing that they are at high risk of being rapists and or murderers.

Act-9: Wealth, Power, and Greed

The Repulsive Betrayal of Man and Woman Kind

Slavery has been around ever since Ancient Egypt and in other countries on the continent of Africa. But there was also a degree of respect for many enslaved people; the slaves were not whipped until their backs were blistered, they were not hung from trees for disobedience for the enslaver's or overseer's pleasure, nor did they have half of their feet chopped off because they tried to escape.

It wasn't until 1619 that the slave trade landed on the grounds of what is now present-day America and changed the slave game and the way they were treated for the next 400 years. This new type of slavery was introduced to the Americas and is said to have been spearheaded by a wealthy governor of Virginia, George Yeardley and his Cape Merchant, Abraham Piersey. Piersey saw and took an opportunity to steal 60 or so slaves from a Portuguese slave ship that was docked in Veracruz, Mexico. He then transferred said slaves to Virginia, launching a new market and trade business for the wealthy landowners. They consisted of English Anglo-Saxons who lived in America. They then saw the benefit of having slaves and began importing, buying, selling, and enslaving African people.

These people - the Spanish, the Portuguese, the English, and the British - all thought that it was a good idea to send their ships to Africa to hunt and buy the native African people. They would then chain them up to the bottom of ships and then send them back to Europe and the Americas, which took weeks and sometimes over a month to reach their final destinations. It is still to this day unclear as to which people should be awarded the gold medal for being the first to have landed in America with the first ship full of slaves.

But the front runner is said to be the Spanish coming into South Carolina in 1526, and then we have Hernando DeSoto, another Spanish slave trader landing in what is now present-day Florida in 1565. And finally we have the Cape Merchant Piersey, embarking in Point Comfort, Virginia with his shipload of cargo full of slaves in 1619. It really doesn't matter who landed first because all the kings in different parts of the world, Emperor Charles V, King Ferdinand V of Spain, King John Aviz of Portugal, and the men they sent to Africa are all equally as diabolical and culpable in the repulsive Slave trade. These kings mentioned above and their cronies, along with their predecessors are solely responsible for what was the massive centuries-long exportation of slaves from the continent of Africa to America, Europe, and elsewhere.

Emperor Charles V, King Ferdinand V, and King John Aviz

In 1518 Emperor Charles V woke up one morning and thought it would be a good idea to send Lorenzo de Gorrevod to the continent of Africa to bring back over 1500 slaves to Spain. It is unclear as to how many ships and/or trips it took to meet that quota. But as a loyal servant of the Emperor, Gorrevod did as he was ordered and fulfilled the Emperor's wishes that year. Although the Atlantic slave trade was well established before Charles V had his vision of thousands of slaves under his command, it was never done on such a scale. Charles opened the oceans for the mass exportation of slaves from Africa to other countries that year going forward. Some 14 years before Charles V decided to order thousands of slaves to work in his gold mines and sugarcane fields the exportation of slaves from Africa to Spain was no more than 5 or 10 slaves at a time. The largest order of slaves shipped from Africa to Spain before 1518 took place and was authorized by King Ferdinand V in 1510. He only needed 50 slaves, which at that time was considered to be a huge demand.

King John Aviz of Portugal, He Too was a leader in the Atlantic slave trade shipping slaves from Africa to Portugal, which began in 1444 A.D. The Portuguese continued this practice well after King John Aviz's reign and in 1526 began shipping slaves to such destinations as Europe, the Americas, and Brazil.

These three kings were not only involved in the Atlantic Slave trade but also increased the importation of African men, women, and children, which continued for centuries. And all three of these men too made sure that many of the Black women that they enslaved were placed as servants in their homes and/or castles and many others were taken as their concubines.

Act-10: Coming to America

Such atrocious acts could not have taken place here in America if not for the wealthy landowners who lived in what is now the Northern and Southeastern United States. Landowners in the Southeastern part of the country held the demand for backbreaking labor for their vast plantations, mainly tobacco and cotton fields. They needed slaves to plant and harvest their crops so slaves were shipped here from Africa and forced to perform such labor under harsh conditions without pay.

In 1789 the first President of the United States, George Washington, decided that He Too had to own slaves because it was just the thing to do and just the way the White man thought about how Black people should be treated at the time. He was just the first of several other presidents that came after him that engaged in this atrocity because they all were afflicted with the deepest degree of the RRKD-G that was passed down from their ancestors for generations.

All of the aforementioned leaders, presidents, and conquerors were for the most part successful because they were barbarians. And many of them traveled far and wide to take, steal, rape, and kill for what they wanted. Those leaders that didn't travel by land or sea stayed in their homelands and financed the voyages and sent others to do their taking, killing, and raping. They just sat on their thrones draped in silk garments and gold jewelry but they too were barbarians.

The fact of the matter is that White people of today don't really want to speak on this behavior because many are truly ashamed and some are truly remorseful. It's just too painful for many of them to think of how the early White men and the not-so-early White men violated Black men and women. Black men and Black women were brutally, heartlessly, and murderously treated by the White man. To this day it is rarely brought up in conversation by White intellectuals or taught in public schools. White men traveled clear across the oceans to take and bring Black people to the Americas and elsewhere for the sole purpose of enslavement.

When the enslaved Black women were raped by the White masters or White overseers at will, they were forced to have the White man's children because there were no abortions. There was nothing said to the authorities about such rapes. Why? Because there was no law against raping enslaved Black women by White men. What thousands of those enslaved Black women figured out and learned was that if they wanted to live a life with some sense of comfort they had to suck it up. They learned that from the thousands of other concubines and slaves that came before them. They too learned that they had to be submissive to the conquerors and the masters of the plantations or they would have to suffer the wrath for being disobedient.

Since the beginning, whenever man became the dominant force and at the top of the food chain he always took whatever he wanted by force: land, wealth, and other people, especially women. The reason is that the degree of the RRKD-G in humans during early times was so strong in men that they never thought about how other people felt or if the people had any feelings at all. It has taken centuries of breeding all around the world for the *Gene* to become diluted in a great percentage of the world's population and to get where we are today. Yet, it is still far from being contained. If we were to go back to the year 1830 one could almost believe that we as humans were after thousands of years just about to make that transition in eliminating the violent and hate portion of the RRKD-G. Unfortunately for thousands of people going forward, that has not been the case.

But in that year, there were more than a few Anglo-Saxon or White men, if you will, who agreed that slavery was unjust and, therefore, unconstitutional and that Black people should be freed immediately. Leading the charge for said change at that time was a journalist by the name of William Lloyd Garrison, who, in 1832, helped to establish the New England Anti-Slavery Society. At the time, the 7th president was in office, President Andrew Jackson, who himself had no problem with having and owning slaves, meaning He Too was under the influence of a severe case of the RRKD-G. That meant that Garrison's pleas for freeing slaves fell on deaf ears, but that too meant the death of thousands of Black men slaves and the rapes of thousands of Black women slaves subsequently.

Again the signs that the RRKD-G in the human race seemed as though it was diminishing in 1832, but it was just a flicker in time because it took another 22-plus years before the issue of freeing slaves was seriously discussed again.

That discussion took place again in 1854 between the longtime activist and newspaper editor Lloyd Garrison and a slave master who just happened to be the President of the Confederacy, Jefferson Davis. Garrison led a great fight for over

30 years of his life to accomplish what he truly believed in, and that was to abolish slavery.

Before America's First President—Benjamin Franklin

There was another figure known in America as a Founding Father but he never became President of the United States and still managed to make his way onto the U.S. currency. His name was Benjamin Franklin. Franklin lived a pretty full life and accomplished several meaningful contributions to the people of the United States and elsewhere in the world by being an inventor. Franklin was instrumental in discovering electricity with his lightning rod experiment and He Too is credited with inventing eyewear such as the bifocals. Benjamin Franklin went on to become President of the Academy and College of Philadelphia, and the man even managed to become the first United States Ambassador to France. It seemed as though there was nothing that Benjamin Franklin couldn't do when he put his mind to it. And that even meant when he decided to become a newspaper editor and printer he did it, and He Too became successful at that as well.

Just by observing O'le Benjamin's outward appearance one would never believe that this potbellied figure of a man with those disarming bifocals hanging on the tip of his nose would be in reality this hardcore slave master. With all the hats that Benjamin wore it would seem like he wouldn't have had the time to oversee slaves but he managed to do so. Benjamin owned 10-15 slaves at a time placing most of them on his property to work and a few he had working at a print shop that he and his wife ran. The print shop was called The Pennsylvania Gazette and it is unclear as to what he had the slaves doing there because slaves were not allowed to read or write.

What Benjamin and his wife did there was print advertisements about rewards for runaway slaves and He Too ran ads about the upcoming slave auctions being held there in Pennsylvania and New York City on Wall Street. Benjamin made a lot of money by being involved in the international and local slave trade as well. He Too would attend both auctions frequently between the years 1750 and 1762. Franklin, in the 84-plus years of his life managed to make a very good living for himself and his common-law wife, Deborah Read, but for the better half of his life, Franklin lived among and owned slaves. This meant that he believed that a Black person was less than he or any White person. To him the right to take, sell, whip, rape, hunt, and punish any Black person within his sphere was just another day at the office.

Benjamin and Deborah both had a deep degree of the RRKD-G, because they worked their slaves all day with no pay and kept most of them in living conditions unfit for humans. Only the Black slave women that Benjamin liked were treated with some sense of humanity and allowed to work in his home, sleep in his bed, and bear his children. He Too failed to support the children he fathered with the slave women he owned, yet he continued to work them as if they were just cattle on his property.

George Washington

In 1743 George Washington inherited from his father, Augustine, over 200 acres of land and along with that land He Too inherited ten slaves. Arguably George Washington was the youngest slave owner pre-presidentship when he was only 11 years old. As he grew into manhood he purchased over a dozen more before becoming president. And if that wasn't enough some 16 years later Washington married a slave master's daughter, Martha Dandridge. In 1759 she brought some 80 additional enslaved Black people into the marriage that she had inherited. These two people not only inherited land and slaves from their fathers but she also got them first from the Custis estate (from where she came) and second from her late husband. They both too inherited a vile strain of the RRKD-G from their parents.

Washington was sometimes called the "Father Of Our Country." Plus he was present during the drafting of the United States Constitution and that may have been a good thing for White citizens of the United States but it did nothing for the enslaved Black people. The reality of the matter is that George and Martha were the evil "Step Father and Step Mother Of Our Country" to all of the many slaves they owned and worked from sun up to sun down. And yes Washington was a general in the army and became a national hero for that but that only meant he was a good soldier, not a good person.

In 1759 George Washington became the first United States President and between him and his wife Martha, they owned in excess of 3000 acres of land in Northern Virginia. Together they worked those many slaves all day and every day to develop and maintain that land for the better part of 50 years.

George Washington had his slaves expand on the plantation during those years making the estate worth millions of dollars in today's market; just 15 acres alone are selling for $60 million today. The reason that the property holds so much value is solely because of the blood, sweat, and tears of the many Black slaves who worked and maintained it all those years ago. I find that fact to be offensive on so many levels because the slaves were never paid a dime and even to this day the immediate family members of the Washington family are still enriched beyond belief. George Washington over those same years found the time to hand pick over a dozen enslaved Beautiful Black women and took them as his concubines. And by looking at photos of his wife it is no mystery to me as to why he wanted those Beautiful Black girls and women. And the sad thing about it is that none of the offspring of the Black slave women George fathered children with (and there were several!) ever received a dime from him or the estate. Damn Hypocrite!

Just because after 50 years of owning slaves and then on his deathbed he suddenly had this "Come to Jesus Moment" and decided to set a few of them free, well that doesn't do it for me as far as excusing him from the decades of atrocities he committed against those Black men and women is concerned. George Washington was the 1st U.S. President and He Too was one of the most despicable presidents this country ever put in office.

Thomas Jefferson

Most of the wealthy slave owners and or plantation owners were not hands-on when it came to disciplining their slaves; instead they hired slave overseers/slavemasters. It was they who ran the plantations and the owners gave them total powers over the slaves.

One such slave owner was born in Shadwell, Virginia in April of 1743 on a large plantation owned by his wealthy parents, Jane Randolph and Peter Jefferson. They named their love child Thomas Jefferson. His mother Jane was said to have come from nobility in London and his father Peter was born in Chesterfield County, Virginia and owned a Tobacco plantation near there. In 1752 Thomas Jefferson inherited 5,000 acres of land which he later named Monticello. Along with the land He Too inherited a dozen African slaves in the deal which made him one of, if not the youngest slave owners in the history of slavery.

At the age of 16 Jefferson attended college and after graduating, he became a successful lawyer. In 1776 he went on to write the Declaration of Independence. Four years before that in 1772 he met and married his wife Martha Wayles Skelton who by way of her father brought 135 more slaves into the marriage. Later on in the marriage she became the First Lady of Virginia while Jefferson served as Governor from 1779 to 1781.

Thomas Jefferson not only inherited Monticello from his father He Too inherited a deep dose of the RRKD-G. He Too believed in slavery in the worst way and proof of that is that he owned well over 400 slaves in his lifetime. In 1766 Jefferson decided to build his mansion on 4000 of the 5000 acres that he inherited so he worked his many slaves seven days a week. His slaves laid down the foundation for what was to become Monticello one of the most expensive properties in South-Central Virginia.

After the foundation was laid some two years later the construction of the mansion began. Jefferson continued working his slaves day in and day out for over 20 years straight. The result of their back-breaking labor was this magnificent and expensive property that stands there to this day. Many of the enslaved people worked all of their adult lives to accomplish Jefferson's dream of having his large estate built on said property. And they worked with no pay I might add.

Thomas and Martha had six children over the course of their marriage, but only two survived to adulthood, which did not discourage Ole Tommy Boy. Thomas Jefferson made sure he had his pick of the most Beautiful Black slave women that he bought or inherited. He Too had a few concubines but He Too had a unique fondness for one of his Black beauties. This particular Black slave woman just so happened to be the half-sister of his wife. Her name was Sally Himings.

Along with crisscrossing the country and writing the Declaration of Independence, traveling back and forth overseas, and being the Minister of France, Thomas Jefferson also became Secretary of State. Surprisingly this busy man still found a way to spend time with his favorite Black slave woman, Sally Himings. The years-long relationship between him and her began in 1786 when he had his friend Mr. Petit escort two of his female slaves, Polly and Sally, to Paris. At that time Sally was only 12 years old and why they traveled there is not clear. But Jefferson after two years joined the two girls in Paris and while he was there with them he began a sexual relationship with Sally.

As a result of said relationship Sally became pregnant. She was just 14 years old at the time. The child only survived a few years but the relationship continued up until he became the 3rd U.S. President in 1801 and beyond. Together they produced six more mulatto children over the years but only four of them reached adulthood. Sally lived to be in her early 60s and died in 1835, outliving Jefferson by nine years.

Out of all of the slaves that Thomas Jefferson owned in his lifetime, and there were many, he only saw fit to free a few of his favorites. He Too had somewhat of a "Come To Jesus Moment," and after 50-plus years condoning the taking, raping, whipping, and hanging of Black slaves he decided in his will to set free maybe 10 or 15 of his slaves. Wow! What a generous gesture from one of the most famous slave owners and statutory rapists of all time.

Andrew Jackson

Andrew Jackson was known for serving as a general in the United States Army among other things, including being elected as the 7th President of The United States in 1829. Before Jackson became president he educated himself well enough to become an attorney and was admitted to the bar in North Carolina. Later he went on to serve in the United States Senate for the state of Tennessee, and from there he elevated himself to the Tennessee Supreme Court as a justice in 1798. It appears that Jackson did very well financially during his years practicing as an attorney and a justice officer in the Supreme Court because in 1804, he came up with the idea to purchase 1000 acres of land. He Too decided that he wanted to follow in the footsteps of Thomas Jefferson and turn his land into a plantation and build his mansion on it, naming it *"The Hermitage"*.

But first, He Too had to purchase slaves to work the land, preparing the foundation for the building of his said mansion. He started with a couple of dozen slaves and after 20 years he ended up with over 150 working slaves. He worked those slaves around the clock with no pay so He Too became a wealthy slave and plantation owner. Once he became the 7th President of the United States in 1829 his stance on slavery never changed. He Too continued to purchase more slaves. Jackson worked his slaves as if they were like the four-legged cattle on his plantation. It is clear that He Too possessed a vile strain of the RRKD-G because he continued to have the belief that Black people were just three-fifths of human beings. I consider Jackson one of the worst presidents ever and a vile human being.

In 1858 there was another White man of means who agreed with Garrison in his beliefs on the issue of slavery, but not completely. In a debate that year in Charleston, Illinois, this same White man made it clear that He Too wanted to see slavery abolished because He Too thought it was unjust. He then went on to state that he believed that slaves should be given their freedom, but he also made it clear that they would not be free to vote in elections or serve on juries, nor were they free to marry into the White race. Three years later in 1861, that very same White man became the 16th President of the United States. His name was Abraham Lincoln. Lincoln was the 16th President of the United States, and He Too was the 1st president who did not own slaves. Unlike all of his 15 predecessors Lincoln knew in his heart of hearts that slavery was inhumane and needed to be abolished, but he was outnumbered in his thinking.

This meant that any movement towards freeing slaves even with the backing of his friend Lloyd Garrison would still take another five years before Lincoln would even get the thought of freeing the slaves on paper.

Before I go any further about Lincoln, I just want to touch on some of the foul acts that a few of his 15 predecessors committed. The one that comes to mind and stands out the most to me is the 1st President of the United States, but we can't leave out Ole Zac.

Zachery Taylor

In 1784 on a plantation in Virginia a young boy by the name of Zachery was born and then raised on it by his father, Richard Taylor. Apparently one plantation was not big enough for Mr. Taylor. So Taylor decided to buy another and bigger one in Springfield, Kentucky, which meant he needed more slaves to work them as well. He went from owning 30 slaves in 1785 to owning another 50 more by sthe year 1800. Those slaves worked his vast land, laid the foundation for and built his house on the same.

Zachery learned the ways of owning, working, and disciplining slaves from watching his father for 20-plus years. Zachery remained on the plantation with his father until the age of 24 when, in 1808 he joined the Service. After his stint in the military he went to Maryland to visit a long-lost friend and on that trip he met a young lady by the name of Margaret Mackall. She was the daughter of a wealthy tobacco plantation and slave owner who lived in Calvert, Maryland. Shortly after that they became engaged and were married that same year. Zachery by this time had become prolific at this plantation and slave-owning business so he then purchased another plantation in Cypress Grove, Mississippi.

Taylor joined the military during his youthful years and became a commander at Fort Pickering, which was in what is now known as Memphis, Tennessee. Taylor's many years growing up and managing slaves on his father's plantation groomed him for his stint in the military where he fought, killed, and took land from the Native American Indians. During his stay in the military he went to more than seven states, Mississippi, Oklahoma, and Texas, rounding up Indians and taking their land. While Taylor was riding across the States commanding his soldiers and playing Cowboys and Indians he left strict instructions to his several plantation slave masters on both plantations about how to discipline his slaves.

Now between his wife's many slaves and the ones that he bought they owned over 250 slaves that they worked day and night in both Kentucky and Mississippi. All of this took place before he became the president. Zachery in 1848 ran for and won the election and became the 12th president of the United States even though he was a slave owner of close to 300 slaves, as the figure goes. He Too inherited a potent strain of the RRKD-G from his father.

This meant he approved of whatever treatment that his overseers of his slaves thought appropriate. Be it whipping the male slaves and even the taking and raping of the female slaves for their pleasure. And what was even more ridiculous is that while being President Zachery adopted some anti-slavery measures. One was that he said he didn't want slavery to spread into the new U.S. territories, but he had little or no problem with himself owning so many slaves. Zackery made sure that several of his slaves worked at and around the White House. How hypocritical is that?

How could this man really believe that people would listen to him speaking against slavery while he himself was sitting up north in the White House owning stables of slaves, including several Black concubines in two different States?

Abraham Lincoln

Now back to Lincoln, as I was saying, it took him two years after becoming President in 1863 before he put on paper what he always said that he wanted to do which was to free slaves. That speech and those writings turned out to be one of the most famous addresses to the American people. It is known as The Emancipation Proclamation, which was supposed to mean that all slaves in America were to be granted their freedom. The problem was that thousands of White men still had a deep affliction of the RRKD-G, and they did not agree with what President Lincoln was proposing back then. In fact it would take another 100 years of continued taking, raping, and hanging of Black people before White people in the Southeastern United States would come close to agreeing with what the 16th president, Abraham Lincoln put on paper and spoke about in 1863.

Although the RRKD-G is in all the human race history has taught us that the rage, rape, and kill portion of the gene is more prominent in men, *White* men in particular. There is evidence of that in countries around the world and it was displayed in Portugal, Germany, South Africa, and in the Northeast and Southeastern parts of the United States. Some 26 years after

Abraham Lincoln signed the Emancipation Proclamation here in the United States there was very little progress with the issue of freeing the slaves; it was just words on paper that carried very little weight. The White men of that era on the East Coast of America were still being born with a high degree of the RRKD-G and refused to relinquish and or let go of the power they held over the Black slaves.

While America was seemingly breeding its way out of the centuries-long evilness of the RRKD-G in the late 1800s it was still divided on the issue of slavery and how the so-called freed slaves should be treated as human beings. This was because the landowners in the South who were all White men still needed free manual labor to farm their millions of acres of land. That labor came from Black slaves and setting slaves free would create a financial hardship for them so much so that they were not willing to submit to the law of the land, willingly, and many didn't.

Act-11: Mad Men of Europe

Adolf Hitler

In 1889 in a faraway land called Austria, in a small town with a big name, Braunau am Inn, there was a young boy born to a couple, Klara (Polzl) Hitler and Alois Hitler. They named their child Adolf. Alois Hitler took after his father and became this bitter man due to the fact his father was born with a severe case of the RRKD-G; He Too in turn became abusive towards his son Adolf. Also since he was born out of wedlock it made Mr. Hitler an angry man. The abuse was both physical and mental; he would lock Adolf in his closet when he would not obey him and would feed Adolf just once a day for months at a time.

By the time Adolf became a teenager, he had grown to hate his father. They never got along and were always bitterly at odds with each other on all issues. When his father suggested that Adolf join the Habsburg Civil Service in 1913 Adolf completely ignored him and decided he would instead join the Austrian military. Much to his dismay he was classified as unfit.

However in February of 1914 King Louis III allowed Adolf to join the Bavarian Reserve and a few months later he was deployed to Belgium and fought in the 1st Battle of Ypres during World War I. Hitler was wounded during his short stay in the military landing him in the hospital but also earning him the 1st and 2nd Class Iron Crosses once the war ended. These awards meant a great deal to Hitler and they gave him confidence but strangely enough they angered him as well. But they were enough for him to want to join a different party, one that he actually wanted to lead. Hitler then moved to Munich where he met up with a former soldier, Ernest Rohm who was a member of a small group of soldiers who welcomed him. After a few months Hitler became the leader of that group and was unhappy with Germany's loss. This small handful of soldiers that Hitler became a leader of was called the DAP or the German Workers Party. By the end of 1919 Hitler turned those few soldiers into a few thousand and then changed their name to Nazis, and became commonly known as the Nazi Party which was anti-Marxist and anti-Semite as well. It soon became clear even though still not so understandable about why Adolf Hitler came to hate Jewish people so much. Some say it was because a Jewish prostitute had given him a sexual disease that he couldn't shake off, and then there was the unproven rumor that the Jews were responsible for a poison gas attack during the First World War.

Maybe it was those reasons coupled with the fact that Hitler's father transferred his vile variant of the RRKD-G to him which would have triggered his diabolical behavior.

On Hitler's path to power he and his closest cronies believed that Germany didn't lose the war on the battlefield but somehow the Jews betrayed Germany and sided with the enemy which was what cost them the war. But after the war the German government investigated and found out that was not the case, and there were over a hundred thousand Austrian and German Jews who fought honorably in that war.

But Hitler's hatred for Jews would not allow him to believe the outcome of that investigation and thus, he continued to make it known exactly how he felt about Jewish people. Hitler believed that Jewish people were nothing more than germs and insects and they should be treated as such. This meant according to him, that they needed to be exterminated. What is known is that in January 1933 President Paul von Hindenburg appointed Hitler as Chancellor. Then in March of that year he turned into an absolute dictatorial power. Along with his closest followers (Oskar Schindler, Alfred Rosenburg, Julius Streicher, Rudolf Hess, and Herman Goring, only to name a few), Hitler wasted no time in implementing his evil plan.

The devious plan that Hitler had in mind was to systematically do away with the Jewish population in Germany and Poland, for starters. In 1936 Hitler took a trip to Russia to visit with his friend and like-minded despot, Joseph Stalin to discuss the business of how to contain and control an unruly population.

Upon his return he assigned a few of his closest followers to oversee projects in different parts of the country; all of the projects were to be up and running by 1940. These projects were the concentration camps that would double as killing fields and/or gas chambers for what Hitler referred to as the "undesirables." Although they included the homeless and the mentally disabled, these projects were mainly built for the Jewish population in Germany, Poland, and elsewhere.

Hitler invaded the Soviet Union in 1941 and started what he named "The Final Solution," which meant he allowed his army to begin murdering Jews on a huge scale. It may have started there but then it spread to cities and towns all over Europe. The mass murders were done by gassing and carrying out mass shootings of all Jews. Hitler sent Schindler to Poland to oversee the camps in Auschwitz somewhere between 1939-1941 and later in 1943 along with Josef Mengele who was sent there to assist him. It turned out to be the worst of all of the camps because there were more Jewish people executed there than all the others combined. As you can see in the 1900s Hitler was one of those autocrats who sent others to go and perform his deadly missions. Hitler stayed home out of harm's way as did the Kings and Queens that came before him.

Mengele was said to be a world-class doctor but it turns out that he was in fact more of a mad scientist who got pleasure in performing experimental operations. Most of his patients were the people in the camps and rather than curing them of any ailments that they might have had he would treat them as lab rats.

Hitler then sent Rosenburg to Munich to build Dachan so that he could have another camp to carry out more killings of the Jewish people. And when that wasn't enough he sent Hess to Weimar in central Germany to watch over Buchenwald, which was another of the large camps. That camp alone over the years held some 740,000 prisoners and more than 200,000 Jews were exterminated there. Hitler later sent Goring to Oranienburg, Germany to run the Sachsenhausen concentration camp that over the years held over 900,000 prisoners.

Before Hitler invaded the Soviet Union he sent Streicher to build and oversee his most prized sight in northern Germany, 50 miles from Berlin; it was named Ravensbruck, and it was built for women only. Sadly those were not the only concentration camps he built; there were a few others within the country as well. Hitler and his followers were possessed with the worst case of the RRKD-G, which made them unhinged and developed hatred in their hearts toward other nationalities, especially Jewish people.

Hitler was not only the worst of the world's mass killers He Too was one of the world's worst hypocrites because while he and his Nazi soldiers were spitting out how much they hated Jews, at the same time they were drinking, partying, and having sex with attractive Jewish prostitutes and concubines. In fact he and his soldiers kept houses throughout Germany filled with Jewish girls and women from Germany, Poland, and France for their exclusive use. If any of the Jewish girls didn't comply with Hitler's and or his soldiers' demands they would face dire consequences. They would be raped and then sent to the ghettos where they awaited to be transferred to any one of the numerous concentration camps like Breendonck, Nordhausen, or Hannover.

The Jewish women who survived such ordeals understood as did their ancestors that women all around the world had figured out centuries ago, that if they submitted to powerful men their lives would be spared. At the same time depending on how much power a man had it seems as though some women were somewhat attracted to them. For some women, and not just Jewish women, power is seductive, an involuntary aphrodisiac of sorts.

It's like what is going on in the wild to this day when a dominant young rogue lion comes upon a pride of lions, he kills the older male of the pride. He Too would then kill the offspring. Then as strange as it may seem, the lioness of that pride would reluctantly submit to and breed with that same lion that had killed her cubs. But why? It is self-preservation. And why do the rogue lions kill the lioness's cubs? The rogue lion imposes his power, kills the offspring of the lioness, then rapes her - if you will. This is in order for him to ensure he spreads his own lineage.

During the late 1930s Hitler's plan to kill and destroy all of the Jewish race had come, at least in his mind, to fruition because by 1941 they had filled up all the camps with Jews awaiting execution or extermination. Most of these people had broken no laws, yet they were all being killed in various ways, be it by starvation, the gas chambers, and being shot and buried in mass graves just because Hitler did not like them.

It is astonishing how one man could have so much power to convince thousands of soldiers to follow his murderous orders. The orders were to pack trains with human beings and lead them into concentration camps knowing that they would never come out alive.

Hitler was only one of several mad men who achieved the kind of power that blinded thousands of soldiers to the point that they would willingly participate in such atrocities. Those Mad Men executed over Five Million Jewish people!

Stalin

Another leader was born to a couple in December of 1878 some 11 years earlier than Hitler in a country not so far away from Germany to the northeast, a country over ten times its size, Russia. The couple's names were Ekaterine Geladze, mother, and father Besarion Jughashvilli, and both of them were less than attentive parents to the son they named Joseph Vissarionovich Stalin.

This is why he, for the most part raised himself. The reason for such neglect was that both his parents were alcoholics and his father was mentally and physically abusive toward his mother which meant that He Too was abusive to Joseph on a regular basis. Joseph's father and mother were living in poverty in a town called Gori where Joseph grew up and became tired of the conditions. At the age of 16 Stalin had enough of the abuse so he took off and joined the Marxist Labor Party. Shortly after that Joseph began doing robberies, and with little success at doing that he turned to the protection racket as a way to earn money.

After being arrested for kidnapping and while serving time for that crime Stalin was abused by a couple of Russian mobsters. The manner in which he was abused reminded him of the abuse his father gave him and he swore revenge on his abusers and their families.

He Too went on to meet a member of Vladimir Lenin's Communist Party while doing his time in prison and was recruited into the said party. After his release in 1917 Stalin decided to join the Russian Civil War, fighting under Lenin's command.

For several years Lenin took Stalin under his wing with the intention of grooming him in the ways of Marxism and Communism in hopes that he would one day become second in command. After a few years of serving under Lenin Stalin looked as though he was on his way to being a leader of the people, a leader that he thought was long overdue for his nation. Lenin saw the potential greatness of his protégé Stalin, but Lenin fell ill in 1924 and began to witness a transformation in the behavior of Stalin. In a few years Stalin went from being a leader for the people to becoming a leader against the people. Lenin made an attempt to curb the direction Stalin was taking the country, but the transfer of power to Stalin was too far gone and Lenin was too ill to do anything about it. He died that year. The passing of Vladimir Lenin left the door wide open for Stalin to spread his way of governing and leadership throughout the country which was the opposite of Lenin's visions.

Once Stalin laid Lenin to rest he began implementing laws that he felt needed to be strengthened and carried out more harshly. Stalin himself was a womanizer and enjoyed the company of many women on a regular basis and encouraged his closest service members to do the same. It was party time under his rule! In a short period of time and being the leader of the country he personally took on several concubines, and He Too fathered children with a few of them.

He Too put together what he called (The Five-Year Plans and Socialism) in the country which was to be a Controlled Command Economy that only he and his cabinet members thought would be a good thing for the people and country. Well unfortunately Stalin was wrong because what happened in the years that followed was famine and death among the people of the country and Stalin's approval ratings tanked. The reason was that although the Five-Year Plans program was working just fine for Stalin, his cabinet members, and his army, the masses were being ignored throughout the country in 1932 and 1933.

What ensued in 1934 was an uprising by the Russian people against the leadership of Stalin. In response Stalin unleashed the full degree of his RRKD-G he had inside himself and took it out on the Russian people. The thousands of people who demanded Stalin be removed from office were dealt with in a way that only a ruthless dictator would deem appropriate. So what Stalin did was launch what he called (The Great Purge), which meant he ordered his army to round up the citizens who didn't agree with him and had them locked up. He really locked them up because between 1933 and 1937 Stalin had built several prison or labor camps throughout the country and a few more in Siberia. And then there were others that surrounded Siberia. One was Tomsk and whenever it became too crowded with prisoners he would ship thousands up north to another camp called Alexandrovsky.

Stalin gave orders to his military to stop and frisk people at will which meant thousands of innocent people were picked up and sent to these camps. Hundreds of others were sent to the camps just because they didn't have government-issued papers or passports at the time they were stopped. These camps held close to 1 million Russian and Polish citizens over three years. Those who were locked up were the lucky ones because many in that same time period were rounded up and executed. The number 600,000 is said to be a low estimate and many of them were buried in mass graves. What is even more macabre and indifferent is that Stalin's RRKD-G caused him to become this tyrant who cared little or nothing about any of his people, and the disdain he had for them only grew with time.

There was an island near Tomsk called Nazina Island, a.k.a. Cannibal Island where the overflow of prisoners from the other labor camps would find themselves. The prisoners were being hunted down and eaten by a tribe of serial cannibals that lived on that Island and Stalin dragged his feet for well over a year after becoming aware of the situation there. After which Stalin gave his commandants the go-ahead to rid the Island of cannibals.

By 1939 Stalin had absolute control of Russia because there was no one else opposing him as they feared being jailed or executed. Stalin's beliefs were embedded in Marxism and Leninism and he made sure that he would share his beliefs throughout Russia and with other countries as well, i.e., Germany, Spain, and Italy. In fact in November of 1940 Stalin sent his Minister of Foreign Affairs, Joachim Von Ribbentrop to Germany to meet with Hitler to sign the Soviet-German Pact. Stalin decided a few months later that he himself would pay Hitler a visit to Germany. So in March 1941 Stalin flew to Germany to see how well Hitler's projects (the building of even more concentration camps) were coming along.

He Too wanted to seal their friendship by signing the non-aggressive agreement between the two countries, or so he thought. Soon afterward Stalin came to the realization that his so-called friend, Adolf Hitler was loyal to very few and to his surprise, he was not on that list.

On Stalin's arrival in Germany Hitler laid out the Red Carpet for his fellow dictator and then showed him around the greater Germany area. He Too began wining and dining him throughout the country and under heavy military guard, I might add. Hitler gave Stalin a grand tour of the country, flying him over Berlin and several of his deadliest accomplishments, the concentration camps. The camps by comparison made Stalin's camps look like miniature versions. He Too wanted to entertain his distinguished guest by taking him to one of a few of his special houses where he kept his most coveted and what to him were beautiful possessions.

These houses were strategic in their placement throughout the city because what he kept within the walls of those houses were several attractive women, German and Polish Jewish beauties. They were mainly there to entertain him, his troops, and special guests.

Over the four-day stay Stalin had seen just how determined and diabolical his friend Hitler was and how badly he wanted to exterminate the Jewish population. This even made Stalin pause.

The reason was that during the short time he stayed there with Hitler he saw a side of him that was deeply disturbing. Stalin really couldn't wait to get his ass out of Germany and back home to Russia. Before Stalin's flight back to Russia Hitler had to show him just one more thing and that was one of a few magnificent mansions he had built or taken for himself. It sat upon a mountaintop near a small town called Berchtesgaden; he named it Kehisteinhaus, which means "The Eagle's Nest" in English. Upon arriving at the compound Stalin couldn't help but notice the heavy military presence surrounding and guarding it.

Once inside they were met with several of Hitler's upper war consultants sitting in the large company room with a few of Hitler's four-legged guards, large German Shepherd Dogs that carefully watched his every move. Hitler walked into the room, sat at the head of his huge long table and instructed Stalin to sit next to him. Hitler then began speaking of his strategy for the ongoing war. At that meeting a couple of Hitler's closest trustees were also present and their names were, Heydrick Himmler and Hans Frank. They were reporting to Hitler about how the massacre of the Jews was going on in the camps.

After that meeting Stalin was all shaken up because as brutal and as feared as he was in Russia he realized that he was nowhere close to the degree of madness that had overcome his friend Hitler. Once Stalin returned to Russia he began reevaluating his friendship with Adolf, and if there was ever really a friendship, the things coming out of Hitler's mouth made him suspicious of his friend. It turned out that Stalin's suspicions were well founded because the mad man that Hitler had become had no boundaries. What Hitler wanted to do was to do the impossible: to kill every Jew near and far. For him to even think that was something he could really do just goes to show how disturbed the man had become.

During that same time there were a few other tyrants who were in the running for the worst of the worst who wanted to rule the world. These tyrants had various degrees of the RRKD-G, and they also killed, had people killed, raped, and imprisoned portions of their population that opposed the way they governed.

Mussolini and Emmanuel III

One other such tyrant was Benito Mussolini who was appointed Prime Minister of Italy in 1922 and remained in office until 1943, ruling Italy with an iron fist.

In 1923 Mussolini began reaching beyond the borders of Italy with his fascist beliefs by ordering and leading his army into Libya on a campaign to get rid of the Libyan people. He Too wanted to commit a Genocide of sorts against the people there simply because he thought one of his Generals was murdered there. But in reality what was really happening and also unbeknown to

Mussolini was that his RRKD-G was raising its ugly head in the most diabolical way imaginable.

Mussolini was appointed to the status of Prime Minister by a man who was small in stature but a giant in politics and his lifetime achievements. That small man only stood 5 feet tall and his name was Victor Emmanuel III and he was the King of Italy. Although King Victor didn't look like it he was one of the most ruthless and ambitious dictators of his time. In fact he was the only dictator in history who held two titles of King.

One was the King of Albania and the other was the King of Italy. And if that wasn't ambitious enough He Too held the title of Emperor of Ethiopia during some of the same years. That little man, King Victor Emmanuel III wore three crowns simultaneously, which was no small feat, and unprecedented.

During Emmanuel III's reign as King of Italy there were several demands and/or outcries for him to remove Mussolini from his post as Prime Minister because of his fascist views and lack of concern for the people of Italy. Over the years the cries to King Emmanuel III to replace Mussolini as Prime Minister fell on deaf ears because of the close relationship these two tyrants had with each other.

The fact of the matter is that King Emmanuel III was the one who had Mussolini carrying out his orders from the throne, thus giving Mussolini the green light to run Italy unabated. The reason Emmanuel had so much trust in Mussolini was that they were cut from the same cloth; they were not related biologically, but they both had a vile degree of the RRKD-G. This meant that raping, killing, and taking were simply second nature to the both of them.

Plus just by looking at King Emmanuel III you would never think that little man had that much venom in that small body. It was as if he was this small house cat with the rage and viciousness of a Saber Tooth Tiger and He Too had his sights set on becoming a world leader. He was already crowned King of Italy in 1900 and years later he wanted more so he and his army invaded Ethiopia in 1936 and took no mercy on the people there. He Too became the Emperor of Abyssinia, but then in 1939 he pillaged it, took the crown from Emperor Haile Selassie and sentenced him to death. And if that wasn't good enough he had the man beheaded and then took his Wife or Queen, Menen Asfaw. Well not exactly. Asfaw realized that being with this little man Emmanual III who was now her King would be better than living a life less than what she had grown accustomed to. So she surrendered herself to him because she simply understood his power.

For Emmanuel III to have given into the demands of the people of Italy and to remove Mussolini from his post as Prime Minister would have been counterproductive because the country was being run just as Emmanuel wanted by his protégé. Not to mention Mussolini was powerful in his own right and had the backing of other well-known far-rightwing leaders such as Francisco Franco of Spain and Adolf Hitler, who themselves were womanizers and mass murderers.

From 1936 through 1939 Mussolini had his military march on Spain siding with Francisco Franco in the Spanish Civil War, which was the first time that Emmanuel III began to question his Prime Minister's decisions. After Mussolini and Franco became partners in the war things began to go downhill from there because they needed more help to maintain their war efforts. They now had to turn to other powers to stay ahead of the game. Emmanuel III was cognizant of Mussolini's prior atrocities and he approved of most of them. Still when he learned about the Spanish connection he became concerned because he wanted nothing to do with that war.

In August of 1939 in a surprising move Mussolini and Francisco decided to fly to Germany to visit Adolf Hitler and spend a few days there, enjoying Hitler's version of hospitality. So now we have three of the most diabolical tyrants that ever lived in the 20th Century hanging out in the same geographical area during a time of war—a perfect target for Allied Forces, only if they knew. It was unclear as to what was planned between Hitler, Mussolini, and Francisco during their visit but soon after the three parted ways. Then at the beginning of September of that same year Hitler invaded Poland.

After Mussolini returned from his unwise visit to Germany a few months after Hitler invaded Poland he made what was to be his last aggressive military move as Prime Minister of Italy. This out-of-control tyrant's last move was to join forces with Hitler. He entered the war in 1940 against the wishes of King Emmanuel III and the Grand Fascist Party of Italy. That act was what forced the King to have Mussolini, his longtime partner in crime, arrested and incarcerated in July of 1943. After all of those years of raping, incarcerating, and killing people near and far this brutal dictator was now experiencing what it was like to have one's freedom taken away. He was taken and held in one of the same prisons that he himself sent thousands of the people he had arrested for little or no reason during his reign as Prime Minister. How ironic was that?

It didn't take long for the news of Mussolini's arrest to make it back to Berlin. When his fellow dictator Adolf Hitler learned about this he began to come up with a plan to get his friend released from prison. After a couple of months behind bars Mussolini was broken out of prison by Hitler's Special Forces and SS Commandos. He was then flown back to Berlin where he and Hitler began to work out and plan a strategy to try and win this war because it was not looking so good on the home front for these two. Hitler was now faced with having to find a position for Mussolini where he could be most helpful to the cause so he decided to send him to Northern Italy to take charge of what was really just a puppet regime.

Mussolini was able to hold his ground in North Italy for 18 months or so until the Allied Forces gained the upper hand in that area. This meant that Mussolini's only option was to flee his post in an attempt to escape capture. It was in late April of 1945 when Mussolini packed a suitcase of clothes, a trunk filled with diamonds and gold which he had plundered, and headed toward the Swiss border. He packed his car and headed north, but not before he stopped by one of his flats and picked up his favorite concubine, Clara Petacci, a.k.a. Deborah, to accompany him on his trip.

The trip that should have only taken a few days took Mussolini and his companion twice that time because they had to try to avoid the Allied forces that were on the lookout for all warlords. But as fate would have it an escape from the path of killing, taking, and raping so many people during Mussolini's years in power was not in the cards for him. And when Deborah decided to continue trusting him and escape with him she sealed her fate as well. Just when it seemed as though Mussolini was just about to enter Switzerland undetected, the automobile he was driving broke down on the side of the road in Como province just a few miles away from the border.

Ironically it just so happened that the automobile Mussolini was driving was a 1944 Mercedes, a German-manufactured vehicle. While standing there on the side of the road a convoy of Allied troops was on patrol and pulled over to assist who they thought was just a regular citizen. To their surprise standing there in plain sight was none other than Benito Mussolini himself. After confirmation that they were talking to Mussolini and Petacci the Allied Forces took them into custody and later that day turned them over to Audisio and Lampredi, two Italian military officers who were based in Dongo.

On the 28th of April 1945, Mussolini and Petacci were driven to a small village, Giulino di Mezzegra where they both were promptly executed. After the execution Audisio thought it was time for the two to be hung upside down by their ankles and put on display for all to see.

It is unlikely that Mussolini's friend and mentor, Hitler, received the news of his execution because He Too had pressures of his own at the same time.

While Mussolini and one of the unluckiest concubines in the history of concubinage, Clara Petacci were dangling by their ankles Adolf Hitler and the second unluckiest concubine or wife, Eva Braun were in an underground bunker in Berlin. It was no coincidence that the heat was on and the gig was up for both of the most wanted warlords of WWII.

This is why Hitler made the decision to take refuge in the well-equipped and roomy bunker to figure out his next move. After being in the bunker for a few months Hitler couldn't take it anymore. Thus he decided to take the coward's way out and take not only his own life but, He Too took the life of his wife, Eva, whom he married just a day before. It only seems fitting that these two warlords and mass murderers happened to die just two days apart: Mussolini on the 28th of April, 1945, and Hitler on the 30th of April, 1945.

Modern-Day Despots

We still have autocratic, barbaric, and murderous leaders in this world today running countries in different regions, i.e., Vladimir Putin in Russia, Bashar al-Assad in Syria, and Kim Jong-Un in North Korea, to name a few. All of those men have a strain of the RRKD-G that won't allow them to care about the lives of others so they incarcerate, torture, rape, and kill people by the thousands to stay in power.

Putin and Assad are the worst pair of tyrants since Hitler and Mussolini of the 1940s. Vladimir Putin is now in 2024, attacking, bombing, destroying, and killing people in the country of Ukraine, and it's without any provocation or mercy. Putin has already collaborated with Assad in the bombing of Syria, killing hundreds of men, women, and children in 2016. He Too sanctioned the attack of chemical weapons in Douma in 2018, killing close to a thousand people and wounding and destroying hundreds more innocent lives. The man is on the verge of completely losing his mind and starting World War III. But why? Because he wants to take land that does not rightfully belong to him, and He Too is willing to kill men, women, and children in order to accomplish his goal. I would argue that the man has already lost his mind and needs to be taken out because he has become a threat to world peace.

Act-12: Back to America

In contrast to the 1900s, 30s, 40s, and 50s here in Southeastern America, when slavery was supposed to have been abolished, Black people were still being treated as an inferior species by White people.

It was still illegal for a Black person to marry a White person and in the Southern states Black people were not allowed to eat in any White-owned restaurants. There were also separate outdoor drinking fountains for Blacks and Whites.

White men could still rape Black women and girls without any fear of prosecution, and it was common to see Black men hanging from trees by the hands of White men in any given Southern state.

The White man in the Southern states in following years after the Reconstruction of 1867 still had unfettered power over the Black population even though there were no more plantation owners that could tell Blacks when and where to work on the Master's land.

The next 30 years were very trying and difficult for the freed Black population, but they persevered and by the early 1900s had built some of their own communities.

The Black population grew within those communities and with that growth and organization came Black-owned businesses in Southern cities like Atlanta, Georgia, Tulsa, Oklahoma, and elsewhere.

Atlanta Georgia

By 1906, the Black community in Atlanta on Decatur Street had established itself as a thriving business Center that consisted of a variety of Black-owned businesses. There were barber shops, Soul Food restaurants, Corner Stores, Bars, and Nightclubs. Despite the tension that was in the air during those years in the deep South between the Black and White populations, the businesses were growing and prospering there. The district of Sweet Auburn catered to all nationalities, Native Americans, Chinese, and Whites as well. As a matter of fact a successful Black businessman in the area owned and ran a barber shop that served and catered to several important White men who came in from surrounding neighborhoods. His name was Alonzo Herdon.

The success of the Black community there in Atlanta didn't sit very well with many Whites and the relations between the two grew tenser as the fall of 1906 approached.

The winds of incitement were beginning to blow over the state of Georgia as if a tornado was headed straight for Atlanta's "Sweet Auburn" business district. If the normal tension were not enough, an upcoming election would create even more thereby sending the tension level near the boiling point.

Two high-profile candidates were running in the gubernatorial election and they both were against Black people having the right to vote. This meant the heat and tension were coming from the top down. The two Democratic candidates were Clark Howell and Hoke Smith, both of whom were against Black people voting and they made that clear by attacking Black-owned businesses through their newspaper connections. Howell had the inside control of the Atlanta Constitution Newspaper and Hoke Smith had a big influence on what the Atlanta Journal Newspaper printed on a daily basis.

Both of these newspapers trashed many Black business owners by printing false reports of Black men raping White women. They too were referring to the nightclubs and bars that Black people frequented and ran as dumps. The fact of the matter is that neither one of the candidates was worthy of being governor because they both were members of and/or were in the pockets of the Ku Klux Klan. Which meant that they too had a potent degree of a vile variant of the RRKD-G to hate Black people and wanted to take or destroy their businesses.

Instigator: Thomas F. Dixon Jr.

In January of 1864 a young boy was born to a couple in North Carolina and their names were Thomas J.F Dixon II and Amanda McAfee. They named their son Thomas F. Dixon Jr. and raised him on a plantation that his mother inherited from her father, along with several slaves. His father joined the Klan during the Reconstruction period following in the footsteps of his brother-in-law, Col. Leroy McAfee who became head of the Ku Klux Klan in North Carolina. Thomas grew up admiring his dad and uncle and He Too wanted to become a member of the KKK when he came of age, with that age being 14 years old.

Thomas F. Dixon left the plantation in his late teens to attend college at Wake Forest where he earned his Master's degree and later enrolled in Johns Hopkins University. While studying there he met and became friends with a fellow student whose name just happened to be Woodrow Wilson the then-future President.

After graduating from Wake Forest he went on to attend Greensboro Law School where he graduated with honors and a law degree. As educated as Dixon was he still harbored hate for Black people that his father and uncle instilled in him as a child. He Too inherited the potent variant of the RRKD-G from his father, uncle, and his mother.

Dixon's upbringing while he grew up on the plantation watching his father and uncle mistreat their slaves coupled with the disappointment of the outcome of Reconstruction just fueled his hatred for Black people. According to him Reconstruction was the end for the country that he and thousands of others grew accustomed to and knew going forward. That is what led him to join the Ku Klux Klan while in college officially.

Dixon later became a Minister for several years and was hired as a pastor in New York City at the 23rd Street Baptist Church. After a high-ranking member of the church accused Dixon of being too sensational on the pulpit he decided to move on to another church. Dixon named that church (The People's Temple) and remained there for a few years until 1899.

Afterward he decided to leave the church altogether and go on a lecturing tour advocating for White Supremacy, something he took great pleasure in doing. While doing that and practicing law at the same time for a few years, Dixon found practicing law to be unsatisfying and a bit too challenging so he decided to try his hand at writing. He then went back to the plantation in North Carolina to begin writing books that he could publish to let people know just how he really felt on the inside about White men's superiority over others, Black people in particular. He chose to do this because he couldn't very well go back to his plantation and resume whipping the Black slaves and raping Black slave women he no longer owned. And yes, He Too was a hypocrite because while overseeing the plantation years earlier he fathered two children from two different enslaved Black women. By day Black women were less than White women, but under the darkness of night he had no problem bedding and/or raping them.

Dixon's hatred only festered over the couple of years it took him to complete the first of his fictional books, *The Reconstruction Trilogy: The Leopard's Spots*. This novel was one in which Dixon wanted his readers to believe that the Ku Klux Klan was the "saviors of the Southern White people" from the "carpetbaggers"—a name given to Northern White people who came to the South during Reconstruction to help Black people.

Dixon also wanted the public to believe that freed slaves were the people who were responsible for the tension and unrest in the city of Atlanta and elsewhere. The second book of the trilogy, which was published in 1905 was titled *The Clansman,* and it too favored the Ku Klux Klan.

The book portrayed Black men as being out-of-control mad men going around the cities, raping and killing White women. And then again Dixon depicts the Klan as these Knights in shining armor riding to the rescue of the White women. But in this case it would be more like the Knights rode in covered in white sheets and white pillowcases on their heads to come to the rescue of people who needed no rescuing. The only thing that was real about that book was that under those bed sheets and pillowcases were angry cowardly White men who were filled with hatred toward Black people. Those Klansmen were all infected with a deadly degree of the RRKD-G and wanted to take and control Black women and murder Black men. There were a few accounts as to what triggered and led up to the riot in Atlanta in 1906. A couple of them stand out as follows:

Many Whites were adamant in their belief that the Black club owners and the nightlife they provided for their Black patrons were the main sources of crime in the city. They even went as far as to suggest that the Black men were getting drunk at the clubs and later going out and sexually assaulting White women. On September 22nd of that year the major newspapers reported that some Black men had assaulted a couple of White women after a night of drinking at one of the nightclubs in downtown Atlanta.

Another account was shared that gave credit for the riot to the movie that came out and was shown in Atlanta theaters on September 18th of that same year. The movie was based on the novel by Thomas Dixon, *The Clansman*.

Whichever account one chose to believe the outcome was still the same and that was on the evening of the 23rd of September. That was when well over a thousand White men and White teenage boys flooded downtown Atlanta. They were filled with rage and hatred in their hearts and were prepared to kill as many Black men as they could find on the streets.

The mob began their rampage on Central Ave. in downtown Atlanta and marched toward the Black-owned establishments coming first to the Black barber shop owned by Alonzo Herndon. They took it upon themselves to break into the shop because it was closed for business at that hour and began trashing the place, smashing the mirrors and windows in the process.

They continued down the street vandalizing Black-owned businesses along the way until they came upon another barbershop that was open with customers within. The enraged mob entered the business with weapons in hand, began beating the patrons with no mercy and left in their wake four Black men dead on the floor of the shop, two barbers and two customers. The hate-filled White men then walked down Decatur Street toward the streetcars, breaching several of them, attacking the Black passengers, both men and women and killing a number of Black men. This onslaught against the Black people of Atlanta continued well past midnight and the only thing that brought it to an end was that the already dark skies became even darker when the dark rain clouds covered the city and released a heavy rain storm upon the city.

The dawning of the following morning not only revealed the devastating destruction of the city and the loss of life that took place overnight but it also shed light on the rage and hate that the White men of those times had for and felt for Black people. It was estimated that there were 20 to 30 Black people murdered that night, while only two White people lost their lives, one of whom was killed, and the other died of a heart attack.

The events of that cold dark night in September of 1906 were fueled by hatred of Black people by the White men who once enslaved and controlled those people for many years. The fact that they could no longer openly and legally enslave Black people, coupled with having to stand by and watch how prosperous Black people were becoming just didn't sit well for thousands of White men in Atlanta and Southern cities.

Let us be clear: Atlanta and the Southern States did not have a monopoly on racial tensions there in the South. In fact racism had spread from the South up to the North and even clear across the country to the West Coast to Oregon and California, spearheaded by the Ku Klux Klan.

Manhattan Beach California

In 1910 Black families in Southern California started building on what became a thriving neighborhood by the sea. The beach property was named Manhattan Beach. As the area became more appealing for Black businesses in 1912 a couple by the names of Charles and Willa Bruce bought a section of the beach for the sum of $1200. Over the next couple of years the family built and grew the first Black-owned resort there that catered to all nationalities: Black, White, and Hispanic. Their business was doing good and the community was growing as well but over the next ten years they were being constantly harassed by their White neighbors, the majority of whom were members of the Ku Klux Klan. Going to and complaining to the authorities was an act of futility because they were supporters of the KKK as well and they too, wanted the Black people off that beach and out of that area.

The beautiful optics and the success of the Bruce's investment in Manhattan Beach was not what the local government had in mind. So in 1924 they came up with the idea to use a law that had been in the books since 1876. That law stated that the government could legally seize private property in order to use it for the betterment of the public. The racist members of the government in Southwestern Los Angeles County set their sights on the Bruce's property.

The law is called *eminent domain,* and it states that if the government executes that law they have to in turn, compensate the owner of the land with a fair market value of the said land. But the White racists that worked there in the government in haste failed to honor the latter and instead, they circumvented that regulation.

That prime real estate was then and still is to this day in Manhattan Beach and the government just took it from the Bruces. The initial reasoning for the Government of Los Angeles County seizing Bruce's Manhattan property was said to be planning to put a Public Park on said location. But the property just sat there untouched for several decades after the seizure took place. The Bruces began the fight to regain their land after they learned that the people in higher positions were trying to lease the beach property to a White racist so he could turn the beach into a Whites-only beach. The lease attempt was aborted due to the relentless efforts by the NAACP to stop it. The Bruce family continued their fight to reclaim their Beach property for decades. Their children, grandchildren, and great-grandchildren never wavered in their pursuit of justice for the Bruce family long after Charles and Willa passed away.

Their persistence paid off and some 97 years after the White racist members of the government of Los Angeles County illegally took the few lots of Manhattan Beach from the Bruce family, they were no more. The new Governor of California, Gavin Newson returned the beachfront property to the Bruce family in September of 2021. That same property that Willa and Charles

Bruce purchased in 1912 for the sum of little more than $1200 is now worth $20,000,000 in today's money.

This unprecedented signing of such a bill by Gov. Gavin Newson and led by State Sen. Steven Bradford was not a reparation to descendants of enslaved Black people itself, but it was a bill to right a wrong of a theft or a taking from, if you will, a Black couple.

For this White man, Gov. Gavin Newson to have sat down with a powerful Black woman such as Kavon Ward, CEO of an organization called "Where Is My Land," and come up with that historical life-altering decision gives me a bit of hope for mankind going forward. Kavon Ward and her organization are currently spearheading other lawsuits in several states in an attempt to retrieve other properties that White men illegally took from Black families years ago.

In contrast, unfortunately there was no harmony in Atlanta in the aftermath of the 1906 riot between the people in power there. In fact the then Gov. Joseph Terrell, or Hoke Smith who was elected governor in 1907 did nothing to bridge the gap between the elite Black and the elite White population in the city. The question is, why not? The reason was that they both were either members of or in the pockets of the Klu Klux Klan.

And they too, were just two more racist White men with hatred for Black people who condoned the beatings, the raping, and the lynching of Black people well before September of 1906.

In fact the White men of Georgia managed from 1860 to 1919 to round up and lynch close to 450 Black men and several women. Only Mississippi rated higher where they lynched more than 500 Black men during the same period.

There has never been an apology of any kind for the riots and killings of the Black people that took place in Atlanta in 1906 from any official member of government, be it a Governor, a Senator, or a Mayor, even to this day. In fact the White supremacists continued their hateful and separative ways unabated for years but at a level the Black population nervously and fearfully learned to live with. Then in 1919 tensions became unbearable in several cities throughout the United States after World War I.

In Chicago that year the White supremacists targeted the Black community and killed 38 Black men and women, destroying Black-owned properties as well. The rioters then focused on Washington, D.C.'s Black community rioting and felt it necessary to murder 15 more Black people there while doing so. To further quench their thirst for blood and hatred the White supremacists migrated south to Elaine, Arkansas where they ignited a riot that resulted in over 200 Black lives being lost, but less than 10 White lives were lost. There were so many Black lives lost on that day of October in 1919 that they named it "The Elaine Massacre," ranking it as one of the most one-on-one violent racial riots ever in the United States, second only to the Tulsa riot that followed just two years later. The RRKD-G was flowing heavily in White men during that year and the next several years going forward.

These three riots had one thing in common and that was a fucked-up reasoning for them even to have come to pass. That reason was that White men thought Black men did not deserve to have the same jobs that were being offered to them when they returned from World War 1. When in reality both Black men and

White men fought in that same war for this country. The thing is that during those years White people, White men, in particular thought and held the belief that Black people were less worthy than White people.

I call it the John Wilkes Booth syndrome which meant that a large percentage of the White population believed as Booth did and hated Lincoln's decision to abolish slavery. He Too felt that slavery should have been reinstated and that's why he shot and killed President Lincoln on April 14th, 1865. Booth was later after a week on the run tracked down and shot to death in a gunfight with the authorities.

Tulsa Oklahoma

In 1920 a state just northwest of Georgia, Oklahoma was one of the first states to ratify the Nineteenth Amendment, allowing women in that state to vote. In that same year the emergence of the Ku Klux Klan was a dominant force in the state as well. In the years leading up to the early 1920s the Black population in Tulsa, Oklahoma had grown and many of the Black people were doing very well for themselves. They created businesses, wealth, and success in a neighborhood within Tulsa that was named the Greenwood District. Blacks owned restaurants, newspapers, clothing stores, and banks. They too had their own doctors' and lawyers' offices, all within a 35-block radius. This area was considered to be one of the wealthiest Black neighborhoods in the Southeastern part of the country, if not the whole United States.

The growing success of the Greenwood District continued despite the fact that Black people were barred from serving on juries and or serving in public offices. Even after serving in the First World War that ended in 1918 social tensions and the anti-Black sentiment were still a problem for many Black soldiers. By 1921 the Ku Klux Klan had recruited 3,200 of Tulsa's 72,000 White residents and they were not happy about the success of the Black businesses in Greenwood. As the membership of the KKK increased so did the apprehensiveness of the Black population in Tulsa and surrounding areas. This was because the "Jim Crow" laws were in full effect being strictly enforced not only by law enforcement but by vigilantes as well. This meant that Black men and boys had to walk a thin tightrope around White people because they didn't know if they were KKK or not. And the reason was that the KKK back then were quick to lynch Black men and Black teenagers. We know that all members of the Ku Klux Klan hated Black people and lynching Black men and teens was their forte.

In May of 1921 a young Black teen by the name of Dick Rowland worked as a shoeshine boy on Main Street in downtown Tulsa where he shined at a popular Shine parlor. He went across the street to the Drexel Building to use the restroom as he did on a regular basis. It just so happened that the "colored" restroom was on the top floor of the building and could only be accessed by the elevator. In those days elevators were run by elevator operators which for the most part, were jobs held by women. The young White woman who was on duty that fateful day was named Sarah Page. She was 17 years old and Rowland was 19 years old. That day Rowland needed to use the restroom so he went across the street to the Drexel elevator. Keep in mind the two teenagers knew each other because Rowland would see Page at least once a day on that same elevator.

May 30th, 1921 was to be a day of remembrance for our fallen heroes and loved ones, but that day in Tulsa was a day to remember how a White man could hate a Black man. The degree of hate that a White man had for a young Black teen that day would result in rioting and killing over nothing more than a lie. Rowland crossed the street and entered the Drexel Building and as he was stepping onto the elevator he stumbled and to break his fall he inadvertently grabbed Sarah by her arm, she let out a scream in response.

That utterance from her turned out to be a scream of death for many simply because a racist White man was standing in the hallway. He was standing some 100 feet away and felt that he witnessed Rowland a Black man, attempting to sexually assault Sarah, a White woman. When the White man frantically approached the elevator using an accusatory tone toward Rowland, the young man just panicked and fled the building. The man then felt it necessary to call the police and report what he wanted it to be, an attempted rape of a White woman. That White man knew that was a lynching offense for a Black man. After talking to Sarah about what the White man told them, the two police officers, both White, came to the conclusion that there was no such attempt by Rowland to assault Page. Nevertheless the next day the police went down to Greenwood Ave., picked up Rowland, took him to the Police Station and held him there for questioning. It didn't take very long for the threatening phone calls to begin coming into the Tulsa city jail vowing to lynch Rowland for the attempted rape of Page. By that afternoon The Tulsa Tribune published a story that read, "Nab Negro for Attacking White Girl in an Elevator."

And if that lie wasn't enough the paper also printed an editorial stating, "To Lynch Negro Tonight." By that evening it was reported that over 500 White men had gathered in front of the jailhouse where Rowland was being held. They were demanding that he be released to them so they could lynch him. By 10 p.m. the White mob had grown to almost 2000 and most of them were carrying guns.

When the news of the crowd being at the jailhouse reached Greenwood, the Black community, 70 or 80 Black men took up arms and headed to the jailhouse as well. Once they arrived they were confronted by the KKK and other Whites Supremacists. When one of the White men attempted to disarm one of the Black men, a shuffle ensued and the gun went off, and the White man was shot. That shot was heard throughout the state of Oklahoma and it was just the first of many shots to come. Both Black and White men began exchanging fire as the outnumbered Black men were forced back toward Greenwood. The KKK and other White men who were in pursuit of the Black men as they were retreating decided that they needed more ammunition and weapons so they began plundering and looting the gun store and other shops in their path. They also began shooting into Black residences and businesses in the commercial districts. They, too, thought it was a good idea to burn down buildings by lighting gasoline cocktails and tossing them into businesses as they marched through the city.

There were many White people who were against the unrest and in fact many had hired Black people prior to this riot to work in their homes as live-in servants and cooks. The KKK and rioters demanded that those White people turn their Black workers over to them and if they didn't comply they too would be targeted. Some of the White employers did turn their workers in but not all gave in to the threats. Astonishingly the racist White rioters continued throughout the night and into the next morning shooting, destroying, burning, and killing the Black residents of Greenwood.

All the Black residents could do was hunker down and try to defend themselves even though they were grossly outgunned. What was amazing too was the degree of the RRKD-G in all of these White people. It brought out such rage, hate, and jealousy simultaneously. This was a rare occurrence but the destruction was large enough that it could be likened to a small nuclear bomb attack. In fact Tulsa was the first city in America that had ever been bombed from above by airplanes.

Estimates vary as to how many Black lives were lost during that riot but they range from 300 to 3000, and over 14,000 were left homeless because over 1000 homes were burned to a crisp. The White racist rioters had made up their minds to kill and destroy Black people and their property and it wasn't something that came to their minds on that one day.

This was a thought that had been brewing over the years because seeing Black people thriving and being successful in business on their own was not a pretty sight for the KKK and their followers in Tulsa. Those people not only burned Black people out of their homes, they bombed and burned close to 200 Black-owned businesses in the 35 square block area known as the Black Wall Street District. It took 30-plus years for the Black population to build that successful neighborhood while many of the White population in the surrounding areas looked on in envy and hatred at what they were witnessing.

It took just one lie by one racist White man to ignite what was to be the worst racial riot in American history. Frankly speaking I'm not so convinced that it was that lie that triggered the riot because I believe those racist White people were going to take, loot, kill, and destroy that community anyway. Why? Because they all had a high degree of the RRKD-G that was triggered by deep hatred, coupled with the fact they could no longer enslave or control those well-to-do Black people anymore, and they couldn't bear to see it any longer.

In less than 48 hours those cold-blooded White men destroyed that thriving prosperous community and killed many of the elite Black people who created and ran that district in the process.

Just as their ancestors had done before them, those White men took what they wanted and killed the Black men and women who they wanted to kill. And that is because as far back as the early 1500s, all the way up to the 1900s they too knew that they could kill Blacks and get away with it. The mindset of most southern White people, White men in particular in 1921 always believed that White people were superior to Black people—a belief again handed down from their racist ancestors. So it's no wonder that the biggest race riot ever in America was never taught or mentioned in history books for over 70 years. There was never any arrest or prosecution for the taking of and the killings of the Black people that occurred during that riot.

One would think that nearly 45 years later by 1964, people would have transformed and realized that the ways of the past, the hating, the controlling, and the lynching of Black people, would be wrong.

Unfortunately, after thousands of years we humans still possess a degree of the RRKD-G that in many people raises its ugly head much too often.

Civil Rights Act of 1963

It took decades and a lot more pain and suffering after the Tulsa riot for some intelligent and compassionate leaders of this country to finally put into law The Civil Rights Act which was first proposed by President John F. Kennedy in 1963. Before he was able to sign it into law he was shot and killed by those who allowed their RRKD-G to drive them to murder. At that time the target for the kill was a powerful White man simply because he wanted fair treatment for Black people, such as Civil Rights and the right to vote. The law itself was not passed and signed into law until July 1964 by the next president who took office, Lyndon B. Johnson. Even after that law was signed it took four more years and two more laws - The Voting Rights Act in 1965 and The Fair Housing Act in 1968 - to end the legal sanctions of The Jim Crow Laws.

President Lyndon Johnson, He Too, signed the "Fair Housing" bill that year after working with one of the most visible and charismatic leaders of the American Civil Rights Movement, Martin Luther King Jr.. Unfortunately for the country and his loved ones, and there were many, King did not live to see the signing of that bill he helped put together for his people. He Too was shot and killed on April 4th, 1968 by an assassin's bullet just days before the signing of the bill.

It is extremely hard to try and sugarcoat this country's history when it comes to race relations and who in fact was the racist here. So I won't even try; I'll just tell the ugly truth.

After the Tulsa race riot and the lack of remorse for such devastation and loss of life it would seem as though that part of the country would have tried to heal itself. Unfortunately, that was not the case and the hatred and racism by Whites toward Blacks continued for decades. Racial violence was the order of the day especially in the southern states.

In the early 1930s there was the continued lynching of Black men by White men. The statistics went from 8 reported in 1932 to an outrageous 28 recorded lynchings of Black men in 1933. Another study or map project called 'Monroe Work Today' was named after a Black sociologist. He put together a comprehensive catalog that chronicled the many lynchings of Black men here in America from 1882 to 1964. And then there was The Auut Studio, which spent four years researching the historical lynchings from that same period. What they concluded was that there were over 4,000 Black men lynched by White men that were documented and that they could prove. And there were more than 450 lynchings in Georgia alone. In 1933 the lynch mob violence and the lynching of Black lives continued for years. The White men also added shooting Black men and boys to death to their repertoire.

Act-13: The So-Called Lone Assassins

The Taking of and From America by White Men and Cowards Emmett Louis Till

In July of 1941 a couple by the names of Mobley Louis and Mamie Carthan Till gave birth to a baby boy in Chicago, Illinois, and named him Emmitt Louis Till. Emmett's mother Mamie was from a small town in Northwestern Mississippi, but her parents left there and moved up north to Argo, Illinois, to get away from racial violence and poverty. Growing up as a child Emmitt never knew his father because his father was executed in Italy on false rape and murder charges. He was raised by both his mother and grandmother living between Detroit and Chicago. At the age of 14, in 1955 his uncle Mose from Mississippi came to Chicago to pay a visit. Mose lived in a small town called Money in Mississippi, and he invited Emmett to come back there to visit him for a while. So his mother agreed to let him go there for the summer. Living in Chicago Emmett had little to no trouble interacting with White people but his mother let him know that the White people down south and in Mississippi were a different kind of experience when it came to being friendly to Black people.

Mamie's decision to allow her only son to take that trip with his uncle to one of the most racist Cities / States was foolish at best and dangerous at worst. In hindsight what happened to Emmitt was the result of that decision and would no doubt haunt Mamie for the rest of her life. They say "Hindsight is 20/20," and looking back on Mamie sending Emmett to a State that had close to 500 lynchings of Black men and boys in the previous 50 years, one can say it was simply poor judgment.

The Supreme Court had just passed the Brown v. Board of Education decision ending segregation in public schools down South. Racial tensions were raw; in fact, a young Black man was shot and killed in Brookhaven, Mississippi less than a week before Emmett set foot in Money, Mississippi.

Emmett Till and his uncle Mose arrived in Mississippi around the 20th or 21st of August where Till met his cousin Curtis Jones. A few days later the family was supposed to attend the church where Uncle Mose was to be preaching that evening. Well it turned out that Till, his cousin Curtis and a couple of other young boys were not feeling the Holy Ghost that evening and instead felt the need to satisfy their sweet tooth. The boys had been picking cotton most of that day and afterward decided to stop by the local grocery store to grab some candy. The store's main customers were the many sharecroppers in the area and it was run by the Bryants, a married White couple, Roy and Carolyn. When the boys entered the store Carolyn was standing alone behind the counter and when Till saw her he just happened to mention to the other boys that some of his classmates in Chicago were White.

Now let us keep in mind that Till has always had a speech impairment and over the years his mother Mamie would have him blow a little whistle before he spoke certain words to avoid stuttering. So when Simeon Wright, Emmett's cousin, heard him whistle in the presence of Carolyn Bryant he freaked out. He freaked out because he knew that Black men were not supposed to whistle at White women, especially in Mississippi in 1955. The events that took place in that Market after Carolyn thought Till had whistled at her are ambiguous, but what is clear is that Till did nothing else to her. He never touched her in any way. But that is not what Carolyn told her husband; she told him that Till grabbed her wrist and then asked her out for a date. Why did that White woman tell her racist husband those blatant lies about that Black teenager? Only her God knows. She knew that her husband and his friends were White supremacists and what they would do to that young Black boy in that town of Money.

After Bryant heard enough lies coming from his wife's lips he took it upon himself to carry out his manhunt for Till. On August 28th, Mose Wright and his family were fast asleep when Bryant and his half-brother, J. W. Milam forcibly entered their home armed with pistols in hand. In truth, in Ku Klux Klan fashion Bryant and Milam demanded that Till get dressed and they dragged him out of the house and threw him into the back of their pickup truck. On their way out of the home Bryant threatened Mose, saying that he would kill him and other members of his family if he told anyone that they had been there and rode off with Till.

What those two White men did to that young Black boy after kidnapping him was nothing short of heinous, and it was all because of a White woman's lies and her hate for Black people. Those White racist bastards went to Mose's home, took a Black teenage boy Till out of his bed, tied him up and took him to a cotton gin. Once they got there they beat that young Black boy half to death and then drove him to a bridge and shot him, taking his life.

They didn't stop there, their depravity continued. Those cowards then wrapped barbed wire and a 70-pound fan around Emmett's body and threw him into the Tallahatchie River below.

Till's body was not discovered for 3 or 4 days after his abduction but in the meantime the word got out in the hood and people began to look for him. The news eventually reached top members of the National Association for the Advancement of Colored People (NAACP), and that is when Amzie Moore and Medgar Evers put their feet on the ground in an effort to locate young Till.

The disappearance of Till was printed in the Greenwood Commonwealth, a local newspaper and subsequently other Mississippi newspapers also printed the story. When Till's naked body was discovered it was so disfigured that it could not be recognized because he had been shot in the temple, and as a result the bullet exited through one of his eyes. When Mamie received the scary news of her son's kidnapping, she screamed, hollered, and cursed at the town of Money for allowing her only son to be taken. In the days that followed Mose phoned Mamie with the horrible details of how those White men took Till's young life.

After talking to state and local authorities in both Mississippi and Illinois Mamie demanded that Emmett's body be sent back to Chicago. Mamie could have had her son buried in her home state of Mississippi but she was not feeling that state of Mississippi and did not want to step foot near there at that time. She had Mose make arrangements to have Emmett sent back to where she raised him for a proper burial. After seeing her son's dead and mutilated body Mamie made sure that he had an open-casket funeral so that all the world could see what those racist White men had done to her only child. The photos of Emmett

Till's mutilated body were published in Jet magazine, The Chicago Defender Newspaper, and newspapers internationally.

Milam and his half-brother Bryant were later questioned by George Smith, the acting sheriff regarding the abduction of Emmett. They admitted to abducting him but said they released him after a couple of hours in front of Bryant's store. The wheels of justice turned really slow in cases that involved White-on-Black crimes if they turned at all in the South. But in the murder case of Emmett Till the trial took place within 30 days. On 23rd September 1955 J.W. Milam and his brother Bryant went on trial and both were acquitted of the murder of young Emmett Till by an all-white and all-male jury. And to add insult to the murder and the acquittal thereof, the all-White grand jury too in November declined to indict Bryant and Milam for the kidnapping of Till, even though they admitted to taking him in August.

Just when you think this story couldn't get any worse both Milam and Bryant sold the True Story in 1956 for a few thousand dollars to Look Magazine, sharing how they kidnapped and murdered Emmett Till. The journalist writing for Look Magazine at that time was William Bradford Huie, who was also an editor and an author who wrote several books and sold 30 million copies worldwide. Those two racist White men were filled with a primitive degree of the RRKD-G, and it only took the hatred of one White racist woman to tell lies to ignite the murderous rage within them.

In 2008 Carolyn Bryant was said to have retracted most of the testimony she gave at the trial in 1955. She stated that, "I feared the reprisal of my husband and his brother if the truth got out"- paraphrasing the award-winning author Timothy Tyson from North Carolina.

Soon after Look broke the story about Milam and Bryant doing the sit down with Huie, other newspapers and news outlets in Mississippi followed up with the story.

Many of the White people in Money realized that they were on the wrong side of justice and turned their backs on the murdering pair. Even the ones who gave them money to help pay for their lawyer fees wanted nothing more to do with them. The Blacks along with many Whites boycotted their businesses to the point they had to close shop. The Bankers in the city would not even extend loans to either Milam or Bryant to plant their crops, so they ended up having to move to Texas.

It is sad but true that here in this country today there are still some White people who truly believe that Milam and Bryant were justified in taking the life of 14-year-old Emmett Till. You might ask, "Why do you believe that?" Well the reason I believe that is because there was a highway marker erected in remembrance of Emmett in 2006 and it was defaced with the letters "KKK" sprayed with black paint. Then there was another marker erected in 2008 at the River Spot where Till's body was found, it was torn down and thrown in that same river. And then when that one was replaced over the next few years it had been shot with over 100 bullets. Then again in 2018 another marker was placed in the same area and it too was shot up with bullets. Only this time a few students from the University of Mississippi decided to pose in front of the bullet-riddled marker with guns in hand and posted it on the internet.

Emmett Till's murder garnered so much attention throughout the country in 1956 that the White Supremacist or KKK had to turn to other tactics to intimidate the Black population. They resorted to driving through neighborhoods, burning crosses on Black people's lawns, bombing Black people's churches, and also started hiring assassins.

In January of 1963 just when it seemed like the human race was beginning to breed itself out of the primitive strain of the RRKD-G, and the hatred and racism was leveling off in America there came the Ku Klux Klan members again raising their ugly heads – covered with sheets, of course. As it turned out there were three other racially motivated events in that decade, which arguably made it one of the worst, if not the worst decade of the Civil Rights struggle.

Medgar Evers

Born on a small farm in Decatur, Mississippi, in July of 1925 was a Black baby boy, Medgar Evers. He was raised on that same farm by his mother, Jesse, and his father, James Evers. Living on that farm meant that Medgar and his siblings had to walk 12 miles round trip every day to attend the segregated school. It took him a while but Medgar went on to get his high school diploma, after which he enlisted in the United States Army. During his service he fought in the Battle of Normandy and after spending his time there he was discharged with honors with the rank of sergeant. When World War II ended Evers further educated himself at what is now known as Alcorn State University. While he was there he majored in business administration and during his time there he took time to debate.

He Too became the Junior Class President and later earned his Bachelor of Arts Degree.

After fighting in the War for his country and then returning in 1945 after his education Medgar Evers had to fight for equal rights for his family, his people, and himself because this country still felt he wasn't worthy.

After graduating from Alcorn Evers took on a job selling life insurance and then went on to become President of the Reginal Council of Negro Leadership. While holding that rank he found it necessary to boycott businesses that didn't cater to Black people. He targeted gas stations that would not allow Blacks to use their restrooms as well as restaurants that refused service to Black people.

After uniting thousands of his followers Evers focused on the University of Mississippi Law School because they would not allow him admission only on the basis of being a Black man. He put the University of Mississippi on notice stating that he was coming to desegregate it and after an eight-year fight, he did just that.

In the interim Evers had become the first officer of Mississippi's branch of the NAACP, which meant he would organize and lead protests against injustice toward Black people throughout Mississippi. Evers's leadership and popularity in the NAACP organization and the success there did not go unnoticed, and certain sectors did not appreciate the direction he was taking. Evers caught the attention of the Ku Klux Klan and White supremacist groups once he got involved in the investigation of the kidnapping and murder of the Black teenager Emmett Till which occurred in 1955.

Medgar Evers was a wise man and he knew he had made himself a target of those racist White groups. He Too knew that his work was important not only for him and his family but also held even greater importance to all Black people here in America, in his eyes.

In the weeks leading to June 12th, 1963 there were numerous death threats against Evers so the city provided a quasi-bodyguard detail to escort Evers to and from some of his meetings and from work to home. On the evening of June 12th, 1963, President Kennedy gave a nationally televised speech that Evers and members of his staff watched at his downtown office. Once that speech concluded Evers and his staff left the office and went to a nearby Soul Food restaurant to celebrate Kennedy's support of the Civil Rights Movement. After the celebration dinner ended Evers got in his car and headed home; he may or may not have noticed that there was not a detail or escort in sight. What Medgar didn't know was that there was a plan set in motion to have him assassinated that very night, and it was no coincidence that the guard detail was nowhere to be seen.

As he drove home just across the street from his house a racist White man was lying in wait with a high-powered rifle. The man's name was Byron De La Beckwith. As Evers pulled into the driveway of his home Beckwith took aim and as Evers stepped out of his car and turned to walk into his home that coward Beckwith shot him in his back, taking his life.

Investigators widely believed that members of the Jackson Police Department pulled off Medgar's detail that night to make way for Beckwith to get away after assassinating Evers. Why? Because it is believed that those same members of that police force were also members of the Ku Klux Klan. That night Byron Beckwith not only took the life of a great Black man, He Too took away a husband from his wife, a father from his children, and hopes and dreams from thousands of Black people within the Civil Rights Movement across this country.

Byron De La Beckwith had been orphaned at the age of 12 years old and was raised by his uncle who sent him to The Webb School, a private boarding school. Afterward he joined and served in the U.S. Marine Corps for a couple of years. Once he was discharged he became a tobacco and fertilizer salesman in Greenwood, Mississippi. He Too then chose to spend some of his spare time in the local White Citizens Council and the Ku Klux Klan meetings where his RRKD-G and racist ideals continued to manifest.

Beckwith was charged and tried twice for the murder of Medgar Evers and both times the all-White juries failed to convict him. Afterward Beckwith would go to his Ku Klux Klan meetings and stand on stage to brag and boast about how he shot and got away with killing a Nigger.

In 1993 Beckwith was living a pretty good life in the suburb of Walden, Tennessee when he got a knock on his door by the State Police. They had an arrest warrant in hand. He was then extradited to Mississippi to stand trial for the third time for murdering Medgar Evers. This time the jury consisted of four White people and eight Black people. Beckwith, a renowned

White racist was finally convicted in February of 1994 for the first-degree murder of Medgar Evers. This time He Too received a life sentence. Unfortunately the coward only lived another seven years but he did spend them in a cage which was somewhat fitting for that heartless bastard. Justice for the Evers family finally came, but it took 30 years after Beckwith took Medgar's life.

Birmingham Church Bombing 16th Street Baptist Church

In the few years leading up to 1963, there were dozens of burnings and bombings of Black businesses and churches in Georgia, Oklahoma, and Mississippi. Fortunately there were no casualties in any of those events. During that same time in Birmingham, Alabama alone there were close to twenty more such burnings or bombings, but by the grace of God no deaths occurred in those cases either. It wasn't until September 5th of 1963 that the bombings of Black churches went from mere scare tactics to cold-blooded murder.

On that day four members of the Ku Klux Klan decided that this time they wanted to take the lives of as many Black people as they could. So what they did was they planted dynamite under the stairway of the 16th Street Baptist Church in Birmingham. Attached to the dynamite was a timer which was set to go off during the church service.

The explosion was so large that after the dust settled rescuers uncovered four dead Black teenage girls and over twenty other members were injured, all Black people. The following investigation revealed the names of the perpetrators and their names were as follows:

Robert Edward Chambless, Thomas Edwin Jr., Herman Frank Cash, and Bobby Frank Cherry. Those four men were responsible for the deaths of the four beautiful young Black girls who were attending church service on that day. Their names were;

Cynthia Wesley, Carol Denise Mc Nair, Carole Robertson, and Addie Mae Collins.

Although the names of those racist White men who took the lives of those four innocent Black girls were known it still took some 14 years before any arrests were made in that case. In 1977 the FBI arrested Robert Chambliss and he was subsequently convicted of the first-degree murder of Carol Denise Mc Nair who was only 11 years old at the time of her murder. Chambliss was the first of the White racist cowards who was sent to the penitentiary for the murders where he died in 1985. The other three White supremacists remained free men until 1994 which was the year that Herman F. Cash died of cancer without ever being charged for his role in the bombing.

Living carefree lives for another 6 or 7 years were the last 2 White racists and perpetrators, Blanton and Cherry who thought they were home-free. That is until the FBI arrested them both.

The then United States Attorney of Alabama, Doug Jones led those charges in 2001 and 2002, respectively and got the convictions for the pair. That was the closing of the nearly 40-year pursuit of justice for the Birmingham 4.

Gordon Douglas Jones 17 years later ran for and became a member of the United States Senate.

Blanton and Cherry were both convicted of four counts of first-degree murder and were sentenced to life in prison. Cherry died in 2004 while doing his time in the Alabama Department of Corrections.

Blanton was not so lucky and lived another 16 years behind bars and went to see his maker in June of 2020 in a separate Alabama Correctional Institute.

John Fitzgerald Kennedy

John F. Kennedy was born to Rose Fitzgerald and Joseph Patrick Kennedy on the 29th of May, 1917 in Brookline, Massachusetts. He was born a sickly child and in his early years he spent a lot of time in and out of the hospital. So much so that at times his parents thought he would not survive past the age of 6 years old. But as it turned out John was luckier than a few of his siblings and made it. He had eight, but four passed away before reaching adulthood.

Rose and Joseph made sure that all of their children attended private grade schools and in 1931 John was enrolled in Choate, a boarding school in Connecticut. This is the same school that his elder brother Joe Jr. attended some years before him. John, after graduating from high school, was accepted into Harvard University following in his father's footsteps. He Too followed his father into politics and at the age of 29 years old in 1946 he ran for Congress and won.

Kennedy set his sights on bigger things, one of them being to become a U.S. Senator, so he ran for that office and He Too won that seat becoming the Senator of New England. While holding that Senate seat in the late 50s, he became interested in keeping the Electoral College and began advocating for foreign aid for some nations in Africa. Kennedy also felt the need to focus on and get involved in the Civil Rights Movement here in America. Kennedy even went so far as to finance or pay for several dozen students and their parents to fly here to the United States from Africa. He wanted to relocate them so that they could further their education. He used funds from the Kennedy Foundation to do so.

In 1960 John set his sights even higher and decided to run for the highest office in the land, the Presidency of The United States. It is not clear when Martin Luther King and John F. Kennedy met but what is known is that both leaders were thriving for fighting for and believed in Civil Rights for all of God's children. And what we too know is that in October of 1960 the presidential campaign was underway and Martin Luther King was arrested in Atlanta, Georgia. The police arrested King for doing what he did best and that was to speak out for the people who were being unjustly deprived of their Civil Rights.

Kennedy also believed that Black people were entitled to the same rights as White people and by publicly announcing his beliefs he was in the eyes of many southern White people just another Irish Catholic carpetbagger.

To paraphrase a portion of one of Kennedy's speeches:

"If an American because his skin is dark cannot eat in a restaurant open to the public, if he cannot send his children to the best public schools, if he cannot vote for the public officials of his choice, and if he cannot enjoy a full and free life which all of us want, then who among you would be content to change the color of your skin and take his place?"

Along with this statement he spoke out against the advice of the closest members of his staff and reached out to Martin's wife, Coretta King, letting her know that he would do everything he could to get her husband released from that Atlanta jailhouse.

Kennedy's campaign staff thought that those statements and gestures would cost him the southern White votes and would prevent him from winning the election. Furthermore it would put a target on his back for siding with and assisting the charismatic Civil Rights leader.

Two events occurred in the two weeks after Kennedy's phone call to Coretta King: the first was that Martin Luther King was released from jail a few days after the call; the second, about ten days later, on November the 8th, 1960, Kennedy was elected to be the 35th President of the United States.

Kennedy was sworn into office in January 1961 and for the next two years as President John F. Kennedy had his plate full. He had to deal with the Bay of Pigs invasion, and he set his sights on the United States being the first country to land on the Moon. Now if that wasn't enough He Too had to make a decision about the Skybolt Crisis and the Cuban Missile Crisis. With all of the supra issues going on Kennedy also had to figure out how to end the Vietnam War that was going on during his Presidency. With the help of his brother Robert Kennedy, who was also his campaign manager during the election and became his Attorney General, they were struggling to steer the country in a positive direction. With all of those issues going on Kennedy kept sight of the Civil Rights struggles here at home as well. He and Dr. King worked closely together on passing legislation on the Civil Rights Act which Kennedy proposed in June 1963 on national television.

115

But even before that in 1962 Kennedy sent more than 100 U.S. Marshals and 30,000 U.S. troops to the University of Mississippi to enforce a court order to admit a Black student and veteran, James Meredith, into the school. That event resulted in two deaths and a couple of dozen injuries. The fact that Kennedy sent the marshals and troops to Mississippi and then, He Too in 1963 sent a Civil Rights Bill to Congress made him very unpopular among many southern Whites. There was growing racial tension all over the south and in May of that year more racial violence broke out in Birmingham, Alabama, starting with the aforementioned 16th Street Church bombing.

Six months after the bombing in late November of 1963, President Kennedy and his wife Jacqueline were in Dallas, Texas on a Democratic campaign funding trip. The Presidential MotorCade was riding down Daley Plaza when all of a sudden shots rang out. After looking at the film footage it looked like two of those shots struck Kennedy, one in his throat and the other hitting him on the back of his head. Consequently less than an hour later President Kennedy succumbed to his wounds and was pronounced dead shortly after.

A man named Lee Harvey Oswald was accused of committing the assassination of the President, but he had an elite apparatus backing him because anyone with a brain knows he did not pull this out all on his own. Not only did he/they take the life of an American President, He Too took away a promising and bright future from Americans and America itself.

Years before Lee Harvey Oswald became a household name he had been arrested at the early age of 12 years old and sent to juvenile detention. After that he went through and was kicked out of over 15 different schools before the age of 18. Later on he was diagnosed as being emotionally disturbed. Now we are to believe that Oswald, all alone planned and successfully carried out the assassination of the most powerful man in the world, President John F. Kennedy, all by himself. I don't think so, and I'm not the only one not to think so either. I think that is why in less than 48 hours Oswald was shot and killed. He was killed because the people who were truly responsible for the death of Kennedy, the powers that be wanted Oswald to be the only person to look guilty. That was a well-thought-out mission using accurate marksmanship by 2 or more shooters that killed President Kennedy, a coup d'etat!

Martin Luther King Jr. Or Michael King Jr.

In January of 1929 a young Black King was born in Atlanta, Georgia to Martin Luther King Sr. and Alberta Williams King, and they named him Michael King Jr. Growing up King Jr. became friends with a White boy his age but they went to different schools. King went to a school for Blacks only while his White friend went to a Whites only school. King and the White boy remained friends until they went off to high school and that is when the parents of the White boy no longer wanted their son to be friends with King. While in high school as a junior at Crozer High King gave his first public speech which was sponsored by the Improved Benevolent and Protective Order of Elks of the World in Dublin, Georgia.

King was given an award for his speech which let him know that he had leadership and public speaking skills so that is what he began to do. King also became involved in the ministry and was mentored by J. Pius Barbour, who pastored at Calvary Baptist Church in Chester, Pennsylvania. King and a couple of his classmates, Samuel D. Proctor and William Jones, were dubbed "Sons of Calvary." King along with his two classmates all went on to preach. King was later accepted into Morehouse College, an all-male historically Black college, following in his father's and grandfather's footsteps.

King met and became involved with a beautiful woman who just happened to be a White woman. They dated for a while, and it became pretty serious, but it didn't last because of the racial aspects and timing. It was just too complicated for the times.

King went on to graduate with a Bachelor of Divinity from Crozer Theological Seminary. He Too continued making strides toward his education in the ministry. King went on to enroll at Boston University in 1951 and while there he worked as an Assistant Minister at Boston's Twelfth Baptist Church under William Hunter Hester. King also went to the Twelfth Baptist Church in Roxbury and served under associate pastor Michael Haynes.

Before King began preaching at Dexter Avenue Baptist Church in Montgomery, Alabama he took philosophy classes at Harvard University in 1952 and 1953. In 1952 King met a beautiful young Black woman by the name of Coretta Scott and after dating for a year or so they got married in 1953 and moved to Atlanta, Georgia. Once they got settled there in Atlanta King began pastoring with his father King Sr. at Ebenezer Baptist Church. Although King was committed to his ministry He Too understood the gravity of the Civil Rights struggle and the need for it to have strong leadership so he stepped into the cause.

King began by taking on the Rosa Parks incident that took place in Montgomery, Alabama in 1955. Rosa Parks, a Black woman, refused to give up her front-row seat on a bus to a White man and was taken to jail for not doing as she was told. Thus the boycott of the City Bus Line, led by Martin Luther King began. The boycott continued for over one year or one year and 20 days to be exact. During that year many White people displayed their disapproval of the boycott through intimidation and violence toward the Black population. Some angry White men went so far as to decide it was a good idea to bomb Martin L. King's home. And if that wasn't enough, instead of trying to find out who bombed King's home the authorities felt it necessary to arrest and jail King, much to the dismay of many in the city. The arrest of King just shed more light on and drew more attention to the whole country of the racism going on there in Montgomery. This too only illuminated King's profile as being one of the most proficient orators ever to stand behind a podium.

King's commitment to the Civil Rights movement was embedded in his heart and the reality of being arrested and going to jail had just become an occupational hazard to him—one that he would just have to pay, and pay he did, close to 30 times.

Fred Shuttlesworth, Ralph Abernathy, and Joseph Lowery, just to name a few, were all preachers, Civil Rights activists, and colleagues of King. Together they founded the Southern Christian Leadership Conference (SCLC).

King stood on stage facing a national audience for the first time in 1957 speaking on behalf of the SCLC organization and Prayer Pilgrimage for Freedom giving his "Give Us the Ballot" speech in Washington, D.C.

King and his followers made many appearances in several southern states leading up to 1963 when he and thousands of other people from all walks of life marched, gathered, and stood at the steps of the Lincoln Memorial and spread onto the National Mall. That march (March on Washington for Jobs and Freedom) was one to go down in history for a couple of reasons: One; it was the largest gathering ever on the National Mall to date; two, it was the day that Martin Luther King delivered his "*I Have A Dream*" speech, which has been regarded as one of the greatest speeches of all time.

Through the next five years King and the SCLC traveled the country marching and speaking out for the Civil Rights owed to the people of this country. In April of 1963 they began in Birmingham, Alabama with marches and sit-ins. Eugene "Bull" Conner, in response to the marchers, led his police officers into the crowd with high-powered fire hoses and police dogs. King was again arrested and jailed during one march and as he sat in jail that time he wrote a famous letter that he named "Letter From Birmingham Jail." This letter is now considered to be a historical document. After his release King and the SCLC regrouped and set their sights on St. Augustine, Florida. From there in 1964 they went on to New York City and Biddeford, Maine.

Because of King's dedication to his non-violent approach to achieving change here in America and in other countries he was awarded the Nobel Peace Prize in October 1964. King was so true and believed so much in what he was doing that he donated all of those funds, which were around $54,000 that he had received from that award to the Civil Rights Movement.

In 1965 King led the march to Montgomery, Alabama which exposed the racism there to a nationwide audience. On March 25, 1965 the march from Selma to Montgomery took place ending up at the steps of the State Capitol where King delivered his speech "How Long, Not Long"— another one for the books. In August of 1966 King and Ralph Abernathy led several marches in Chicago to protest against unfair housing in the suburbs there. One of those marches there too gained national attention and made the evening news. The march that took place in the suburb of Marquette Park made the news because the marchers were met with screaming and violence from the White residents there. The screaming was just the beginning, and then the White crowds started throwing bottles and bricks at the marchers. In one incident King was struck and injured by one of those bricks or bottles, but he continued to march on.

King, being a man who believed in peaceful solutions and someone who was against the war in Vietnam, spoke out against it in April of 1967. King believed that the financing of the Vietnam War was money that should have been spent here in the United States to help the citizens who were in need across this country. So in the following year 1968, King, Rev. Jesse Jackson, and future civil rights leader John Lewis along with a number of other members of the SCLC organized the "Poor People's Campaign."

To let the truth be known after gaining the international recognition he was receiving Rev. Martin Luther King too was on par with becoming the first Black Democratic Nominee for President of the United States, if not winning the presidency itself. The southern White racists that held power too, saw what was to them the scary possibility that King's rise to prominence would raise him to that level. We also can't forget that there were White racist in states such as Chicago and North Carolina, who were fiercely and violently against the Civil Rights Movement. Some of those White racists took it upon themselves to get rid of the threat by hiring a fixer or hitman, if you will, to fly to Memphis, Tennessee, to do their bidding.

Who did they hire? Well the asshole's name was James Earl Ray. He Too laid in wait, not in the bushes as did his cowardly counterpart, Byron De La Beckwith when he shot and killed another giant of the Civil Rights Movement in Medgar Evers.

No, He Too laid in wait, but in a toilet room, which was fitting for him because he was a piece of shit! The toilet he stood on was across the street from the Lorraine Motel. That White racist coward remained boarded up in that toilet room for hours until he was able to get a clear shot at King on the balcony of the motel. When he stood on that toilet and took that shot on April 4th, 1968 he took out one of America's most honorable and beloved Black leaders, Martin Luther King Jr.

King was just standing on the balcony of the said motel just talking to his friends when that coward shot him.

After the announcement of King's assassination aired on the national news there was this tsunami effect, if you will, of anger and rioting that swept across the country from Washington, D.C., to Seattle, Washington.

James Earl Ray was born in March of 1928 to a racist mother and father. They were living from trailer to trailer in Alton, Illinois until they had to relocate to Ewing, Missouri. Ray left there when he turned 16 years old and went back to Alton and got a job tanning shoes. At the age of 17, Ray joined the U. S. Army, and in less than two years he was discharged because he could not adapt to the ways of the service. When Ray returned home to Alton he could not hold a job so he decided to turn to robbing cafes for a living which landed him in jail several times over a few years. In 1959 Ray went to St. Louis where he thought he had perfected his robbery skills but he landed a 20-year sentence for robbing two grocery stores. Ray served 7-years in the Missouri State Penitentiary for said crimes before he figured out a way to escape in 1967 and traveled from state to state and Mexico aimlessly.

Miraculously Ray ended up in Memphis, Tennessee, in a hotel right across the street from where Martin Luther King just happened to be staying; go figure.

Three months, two weeks, and four countries after Ray shot and took King's life the F.B.I. finally arrested him in London and brought him back to the States for trial.

Ray was tried, found guilty, and then sentenced to 99 years behind bars for the murder of the Civil Rights Icon, Martin Luther King Jr. Just days before his death, King's son, Dexter, visited him. Ray told Dexter that he was not the man who shot his father, and Dexter said that he believed Ray.

James Earl Ray died in a Nashville, Tennessee hospital on April 23rd, 1998 exactly 30 years to the month after he took King's life.

Robert Francis Kennedy

After the assassination of his brother, John F. Kennedy, Robert Kennedy too as a supporter of the Civil Rights Movement He Too continued to work with then-President Lyndon B. Johnson to put it into law as his brother promised he would do before he was killed. In 1964 Robert ran for election and won the New York Senate Seat and after that, he continued his advocating for the Civil Rights Movement.

He spoke about social justice here and abroad in places like Latin America and South Africa. Kennedy then threw his hat in the ring to become a candidate for the presidency of the United States, as did his brother in 1960. He Too was running on many of the same issues as his brother John, but just as the southern White people didn't like his brother, they too didn't like Robert either.

But in June of 1968 he went on to win the California primary and it looked as though he would be a shoo-in for the Democratic choice for president. But as fate would have it he didn't even make it out of California with that win because a man named Sirhan Sirhan was in the building. Sirhan thought Kennedy was a bit too friendly with Israel and Black people so he decided to shoot him and take his life.

In 1969 Sirhan was found guilty of first-degree murder and was sentenced to death, at first. After a year or two it was changed to life in prison. Sirhan had been locked up since that time. Sirhan went to the parole board requesting to be paroled 16 times and was finally granted his wish in 2022. A strange but true fact is that Robert Kennedy Jr., who was just an infant when his dad was shot and killed, was in favor of the release of his father's murderer on parole after Sirhan had spent 53 years behind bars.

Sirhan was born in Palestine in March of 1944 and later became a Jordanian citizen. While growing up there he witnessed unthinkable violence during the war between Israel and Arabs. He Too witnessed a Israeli military truck hit and kill his brother and he never got over that image in his head.

Sirhan and his family immigrated to America when he was only 12 years old. The family settled in California where he was enrolled in John Muir High School in Pasadena, California. After four years there he transferred to Pasadena City College. Even while studying here in America Sirhan continued to follow the conflict between the Arabs and Israelis which awakened his dormant RRKD-G, fueling his racist views and anger toward Israel and anyone supporting them.

Sirhan Bishara Sirhan was just one of four men in the 1960s who chose to shoot and take the lives of high-profile leaders of this country. And as a result of each of these despicable acts they committed, each one played a major role in changing the course of this country and arguably the world.

Before they were hired to shoot and take the lives of all these men they were just living average and or less-than-average existences. That is until they took those fatal shots and took the lives of honorable men. All of the mentioned acts of atrocity stem from hatred and racism of the deepest form which had been taught and or learned for generations.

It wasn't until the mid-1970s that more intelligent people laid down stricter laws and came to the realization that racism and hatred had no place in a civilized society.

This is not to say that we as a people have bred out of the RRKD-G or its variants and the ugliness that results from them, not by a long shot. That is simply because even to this day there are countless numbers of dangerous, racist, and sex-craved individuals roaming this earth.

Edwin T. Pratt

Hatred White supremacy, and racism raised their ugly heads again against another Black man. This time they made their way to the Pacific Northwest. Their target this time was another Civil Rights leader by the name of Edwin T. Pratt. Pratt was born in Miami, Florida in December 1930.

After graduating from high school he went on to get his Bachelor's degree in Atlanta, Georgia at Clark College. After a brief break Pratt went on to achieve his Master's Degree in social work from Atlanta University. Once Pratt graduated he was eager to put to work his academic skills so he flew to Cleveland, Ohio to join and work for the Urban League there. After a short stint there in Ohio a position came up for him in Kansas City, Missouri so he took that promotion and spread his knowledge and skills there helping and guiding many people.

Pratt realized that his skills were needed in the Northwest so he relocated to Seattle, Washington in 1956 and, in time, became Community Relations Secretary of the Urban League. Within five years of being in Washington State in 1961 Pratt was promoted to Executive Director of The Seattle Urban League. Pratt was passionate about his work and thrived on helping the people in whatever State he worked in. There in Seattle he was able to put in place The Trian Plan, which desegregated the Seattle Public School System. He Too, spearheaded the Equal Housing Opportunity Program for the less fortunate and the city was on a good path under his leadership.

Pratt stayed in touch with and worked alongside Medgar Evers, Martin L. King, John Lewis, and other giants during the height of the Civil Rights Movement. The assassinations of Medgar and Martin hit Pratt so profoundly that he knew he had to continue the struggle because it was so important. He could have just closed the shop and walked out on all of the hard work and progress that the Movement had accomplished and no one would have blamed him. But no! After Pratt paid his respect to and buried his friend Martin L. King in April of 1968 he continued working for the people and for his fellow leaders who gave their lives for the Movement.

In January 1969 just nine months after a White man took the life of Martin L. King Jr. two other White men laid in wait for Edwin Pratt to come to his home in Shoreline, Washington. Sadly it was reminiscent of a similar tragedy that occurred six years earlier in Mississippi with the assassination of his friend and colleague, Medgar Evers. As Pratt walked in front of his home witnesses said a White man approached Pratt from behind and shot him, taking his life. Unfortunately, witnesses did not get a clear view of the shooter as he fled the scene in a waiting car and to this day, no one has been charged with Pratt's murder.

Seattle, Washington has not forgotten the hard work and dedication that Edwin Pratt bestowed on the city. In memory of him they named two centers after him, Pratt Fine Arts Center and Edwin Pratt Early Learning Center.

Those racist White cowards not only took another great man's life, They Too took a husband from his wife, a father from his son, a father from his daughter, and another Black leader from this country and that community, and that will be something that will never be forgotten or forgiven.

Act 14: A Man Possessed with the Prehistoric (RRKD-G)

Unfortunately we do not live in a perfect world and there are seen and unforeseen dangers that we have to, as humans, be aware of while going through our daily lives. The good thing about this World we live in is that there are hundreds of millions of good, level-headed, and smart people all around us. With that being said we can take some comfort in knowing that the number of people who would seek to do us harm are only in the thousands. The names that are about to appear are just a few of the kinds of people that men, and especially women, should avoid going forward.

The reason is that although the names are of those who have been caught and or dead, there are more out there and it could mean either life or death for those of us who are not careful. While most humans are wired in a way that their degree of the RRKD-G will never rise to the level of harming others, there are thousands who will not only do harm but also kill you. These types of people can be found all over the globe and they would bring harm to you, rape you, beat you, and in the worst cases, might even kill you, dismember you, and then even eat your body parts. This brings us to a man possessed with the Prehistoric RRKD-Gene.

Jeffrey Dahmer

It was in 1960 in Milwaukee, Wisconsin Joyce Annette and Lionel Dahmer brought a child into this world whom they named Jeffrey. Lionel Dahmer was of German ancestry while Joyce was of Irish ancestry. Jeffrey's father Lionel was not always around while he was growing up and his mother Joyce though physically there was mentally absent which made Jeffrey feel abandoned. In his teenage years Jeffrey began collecting skeletons of small animals, placing them in jars of formaldehyde and storing them in the garages of the homes they moved to. Lionel just thought his son was on his way to becoming a scientist or some shit but he had no idea about what was really going on in Jeffrey's mind or where those skeletons came from.

After graduating from high school Dahmer enlisted in the U.S. Army. After a couple of years in the Army in 1981 he earned an honorable discharge. After traveling from state to state for five or six years Dahmer moved in with his grandmother in Milwaukee for a short while. While he was staying there with her he committed a couple of murders.

One of Dahmer's first known victims, according to him, was a 24-year-old man whom he met in a bar in 1987; his name was Steven Tuomi. Dahmer lured him up to his hotel room and after drugging the man he just had sex with, he killed him. According to Dahmer, when he woke up the next morning the man was lying in bed dead and he didn't remember killing him. So what he did was went out and bought a large suitcase, then he stuffed that young man's body in it. He then took him to his grandmother's home and stored him in her basement.

After a few days Dahmer had to figure out what to do with the body. So what came to his mind then was: "I'll just chop his head off and dismember him." And that was exactly what he did; he decapitated the man and then cut off both arms and legs and before putting all the body parts in separate garbage bags, he fileted the thighs. After spending a couple of hours trying to clean up the mess he took the parts and put them in dumpsters around the hood, but he kept the thighs and head. The young man's body parts were never found.

Some two weeks later Dahmer met Richard Guerrero, a 22-year-old bisexual at a gay nightclub. He Too invited him over to Grandma's house for sex. The young man accepted the offer and went to the house with him and once the act was done, Dahmer chopped him up too.

Eventually his grandma became uncomfortable with the hours and the company Dahmer was keeping so she kicked his ass out. Dahmer then moved and rented a furnished unit across town in the Oxford Apartments and in his luggage along with his clothes, was the mummified head of one of his victims.

Now that Dahmer was away from his grandmother's home and in his own man cave he had the freedom and privacy to sharpen up his deadly skills and his knives as well. By this time Dahmer had already committed 4 or 5 killings and decapitations and he wasted no time christening his new dwellings.

Once he placed the severed head of his fifth victim Anthony Sears which he had kept for weeks, on the top shelf of his bedroom closet, he set out to add other trophies to his collection. So in May of 1990 a month or so after settling in Dahmer went out to a Gay Club where he met a young male sex worker by the name of Raymond Smith. Again Dahmer turned up his charm and for the sum of $40 they both agreed to go to Dahmer's apartment to engage in sexual acts. Afterward Dahmer drugged Smith and killed him and then proceeded to dismember him in his bathroom. Afterward he put parts of Smith's legs and arms in a huge iron pot and boiled them in Soilex. He Too, took Smith's head, put it in a huge glass jar and then placed it next to Sears's head up on the closet shelf.

The name Smith is quite common but what were the chances that Dahmer would catch two gay Smiths in his deadly web in just one month? Well that is just what he did exactly because in June of 1990 he met another Smith. Edward was the other unlucky young man's name. Again Dahmer approached the young man and pitched him his usual date idea and unfortunately the man went for it. As the story goes he killed the man, raped the body, and then cut him up and placed his parts in the freezer for a couple of months.

Dahmer's next victim was a young man from Chicago who went by the name Ernest Miller. He and Dahmer agreed to go to Dahmer's man cave to engage in sex for a fee. Well needless to say Ernest was never seen alive again or at least in one piece. Dahmer killed the man, dismembered him, cut out his heart, and fileted his biceps. After separating the body parts that he wanted to discard, Dahmer then wrapped up the parts he wanted to keep in plastic. He then put some parts in the refrigerator and others in the freezer until he was ready to eat them. The depth of Dahmer's RRKD-G had fallen back to a Prehistoric level because he not only killed and dismembered people, He Too enjoyed devouring them.

By the time the authorities caught on to Dahmer's gory activities that he had going on in his man cave he had already killed, frozen, and chopped off the heads of at least 15 young men, 13 of whom were Black. Dahmer a White man took the lives of all these Black men, and for what? Just so he could satisfy his sexual and culinary prowess? Well, in the end Dahmer was murdered by a Black man while he was doing time in the Columbia Correctional Institute, serving 15 life sentences.

Dylann Storm Roof

In April of 1994 a young boy was born to a couple named Franklin and Amy Roof in South Carolina whom they named Dylann Roof. Dylann's upbringing was not terribly abusive but he witnessed his father verbally and physically abusing his mother and stepmother.

Dylann attended White Knoll High School in Lexington and six others in a 7-year period. He Too began using a variety of drugs and alcohol during his high school years which led him to drop out in 2010. He Too was diagnosed as having "obsessive-compulsive behavior" the same year. It has been said that Dylann began studying and/or practicing his White Supremacy and Neo-Nazism Movements by going online and "self-radicalizing." But it didn't take him long to submerge himself into those movements in the worst way.

Racism and hatred are taught behaviors so perhaps the people that raised Dylann should bear some of the responsibility for his beliefs. There are thousands of other people who believe in White supremacy but they don't go out and kill others only based on their feelings. Dylann had an underlying condition, a deep degree of the RRKD-G that sent him into an uncontrollable rage and hate that he acted upon.

This damn fool took it upon himself to just walk into Emanuel African Methodist Episcopal Church in Charleston, South Carolina on June 17, 2015 to do devastating carnage. Dylann walked into the church and sat there for a short time and even spoke to several of the people in the church. Then, all of a sudden he just stood up and began shooting. That day he took the lives of nine innocent Black people while they were in prayer.

Dylann is just another example of what White men have done for hundreds of years and that is taking the lives of Black people, be it by shooting, whipping, or hanging them to death. Dylann carrying on his ancestors' legacy landed himself in the United States Penitentiary in Terre Haute, Indiana and is now awaiting execution.

It is important to reiterate the fact that all humans possess the RRKD-G, but the important thing to note is that most are able to live without it coming out to the degree where one loses complete control of oneself and feels the need to kill others. And let us be clear: anger is one thing, but being violent toward other people is unacceptable. Fortunately only a small percentage of the population carries that degree of the RRKD-G that takes them to that dark place of uncontrollable madness with no avenue of return.

Payton S. Gendron

As the years go by here in America it seems as though there are more and more mass shootings. It also seems that the perpetrators are getting younger and younger with each incident. A case in point is the incident on May 14, 2022 when an 18-year-old racist White male drove close to 4 hours from his home in Conklin, New York roughly 200 miles from Buffalo, New York, to execute Black people. The young man who committed this heinous act was identified as Payton S. Gendron.

He drove himself to a predominantly Black area in Buffalo to the Tops Grocery Store on Jefferson Avenue. He then stepped out of his car with a high-powered weapon in hand and just started shooting any Black person within his range. This young White boy a White Supremacist at the tender age of 18, decided to buy an AR-15-style rifle for the sole purpose of killing Black people. This Son of a Bitch had the audacity to kill Black people but couldn't pull the trigger on himself. He was born with the RRKD-G, but who taught him to hate? That White racist coward shot and killed ten innocent Black people and wounded three others while they were just shopping for their families.

Frankly speaking, I feel like there should be a law from this day forward that anyone who commits a mass shooting like what Gendron and Roof did, and any coward that decides to do it should be shot on the spot even if they surrender. If not, they should be arrested and executed without a trial within a week because the police would know they did it, but who cares *why* the coward did it? There have been way too many of those mass shootings in the last few years and for families of the victims to have to go through long drawn-out trials is a waste of time according to me. Just execute those misfits and get it over with.

Moses Sithole: A BC Killer in South Africa

In 1964 a child was born in South Africa and his parents named him Moses. Little did they know the child would not be anything close to the Biblical Moses that they named him after.

Unfortunately the mother's high hopes for her son were weakened because she was dealing with his father who was a very abusive man toward her and Moses.

Growing up Sithole became disenchanted with women at an early age because his father died, his mother left him and he never saw her again. She left him in a small township called Gauteng and then he, his brother, and his sister were placed in an orphanage where he was abused for several years.

Sithole eventually escaped from the orphanage as a teenager and was later alleged to have committed a few rapes which landed him in jail where he served seven years. By the time he was released from his lengthy stay in prison, Sithole was a very angry man with vengeance in his mind. Ironically in 1993 Sithole joined an organization that was devoted to the feeding and placement of children who had been abused and/or abandoned. Sithole's duties in the organization were to recruit others to help with the children because there were so many who needed help. For two years Sithole would interview women for positions in the organization and would hire some but in the course of doing so he would recall others for a second interview. He would then take those women to remote places under the pretense they were going to be hired but when they arrived at the destination he would rape and kill them.

Sithole began his killing spree in Atteridgeville, later moving to Boksburg and then choosing to move to Cleveland for the rest of his kills. By 1995 Sithole had claimed close to 30 victims, all Black women. Most of his kills were committed in Boksburg and it gained the attention of President Nelson Mandela. Mandela then appealed to the SAPS—South African Police Service. The police then stepped up their investigation to help find out what had happened to all of these women.

Shortly after that Mandela appeared on National Television to tell the people that Sithole had been shot and captured in Johannesburg and while in the hospital he was found to be HIV positive.

When Sithole was finally questioned about the murders he had committed over the years he admitted that he had killed all of those women. Sithole said he killed women because of the few women that falsely accused him of rape years ago, which cost him seven years in prison.

The fact of the matter is that He Too was, and still is afflicted with a deep degree of the RRKD-G and needs to be kept out of society for the rest of his miserable life. In 1997 after a two-week trial Sithole was convicted of 38 murders and 40 rapes. Judge David Carstairs sentenced his Black ass to 2,410 years only because the death penalty had been abolished in South Africa a couple of years earlier.

Theodore Robert Cowell/Bundy

In Burlington, Vermont, in 1946 a young woman by the name of Eleanor Louise Cowell gave birth to a baby boy that she named Theodore Robert Cowell. There were questions as to who his real biological father was because there were three possibilities, or so it was said. For the first few years of Cowell's life he lived with his grandparents in Philadelphia who raised him as if he were their son in order to protect their daughter from scandal.

In 1951 Eleanor took Theodore and moved to Tacoma, Washington and that is where she met and went on to marry Johnny Bundy. Over the course of several years Johnny and Eleanor had four more children, but Theodore didn't feel like he was a part of the family even though Bundy had legally adopted him. But as a teenager Theodore took the last name of Bundy because he said he hated the name Cowell.

In 1965 Bundy enrolled in The University of Washington and while there he met a young beauty by the name of Stephanie. The couple stayed together for a couple of years.

Stephanie left his ass when they were living in Miami and she flew back to her family in California because she said Bundy was too immature and had no solid goals. Her leaving him must have been some sort of a wake-up call because in 1970 Bundy flew back to Washington State and enrolled into the University of Washington once again.

Bundy became an honor student majoring in psychology and went on to graduate in 1972. Impressed by Bundy's abilities the faculty at the UW hired him as an Assistant to the Chairman of the Washington State Republican Party. Bundy went on to enroll in two different law schools, Seattle University School of Law in 1973 and then the University of Utah the same year.

By mid-1974 Bundy dropped out of the University of Utah and drove back to Seattle and He Too dropped out of the Seattle Law School there. Strangely not long after Bundy dropped out of college there young women started coming up missing in Washington and Oregon. Bundy, now feeling the heat in the

Northwest, jumped in his light-colored Volkswagen Beetle and headed east leaving several dead young women in his wake.

Passing through Idaho on his way to Utah Bundy picked up a young female hitchhiker and after spending the night with her in a motel he decided to rape her before taking her life. He Too dismembered her. Afterwards Bundy got back on the highway and drove on to Salt Lake City and decided he wanted to study further so he re-enrolled at The University of Utah.

On a weekend in January of 1975 Bundy took a drive from Utah to Snowmass Village in Colorado where he continued his murderous spree. He departed there leaving behind the nude body of a young nurse by the name of Caryn Eileen Campbell. Two months after he killed Campbell Bundy drove to Vail, Colorado where he met a young ski instructor whose name was Julie Cunningham. After raping and killing that beautiful woman Bundy again got on the highway and drove to Rifle, Colorado with the dead body of Julie in the trunk and he then dumped her body in a wooded area there.

Bundy then drove six hours back to Salt Lake City for a couple of weeks while attending his classes there. There must have been something about Cunningham that stuck with Bundy because after a couple of weeks in Salt Lake he again drove back to Rifle just to check on her remains. Once Bundy eased his mind regarding Cunningham's disposition he simply urinated on her corpse and again left her there to continue to decay.

One would never know just by looking at Bundy's outward appearance that he would be this sick, murderous individual with one of the darkest variants of the RRKD-G. The very next month in April of 1975 Bundy drove to a small city, Grand Junction, Colorado where he picked up and murdered a young woman by the name of Denise Oliverson who turned out to be Bundy's 15th documented murder. The number of women and teenage girls Bundy ended up being convicted of murdering was 20, but he was said to have confessed to many more.

He Too confessed on a few occasions to revisiting a few of his victims and having sex with their corpses and too applying makeup on some of them. Bundy was executed for his crimes in 1989 and was subsequently cremated. His ashes were dumped somewhere in Florida, unknown to anyone but the dumper.

Before Bundy's heated demise he felt the need to assist the Seattle, Washington, Police Department in their investigation involving another woman hater and serial killer. One reason for this was that He Too was simultaneously killing women during Bundy's killing spree in the State of Washington. Second, Police were looking to blame Bundy for some of those killings which caused the total number of women to surpass those that Bundy had confessed to killing.

The difference between Bundy and the unknown killer was that Bundy was an international killer; he traveled from state to state murdering women while the unknown killer stayed in the State of Washington to hunt his prey.

Gary Leon Ridgway

Unfortunately here in the United States and most other countries there are hundreds and maybe even thousands of men who hate women for some unexplained reason. This is something

I will never understand. Fortunately 97% of those men don't act out on their hatred and avoid harming women because the degree of their RRKD-G is so low that it is of no real danger to others. Then again there are 3% of the women haters that are indeed dangerous to any woman that they may come across. In most of those cases the encounters usually result in the death of the woman. The hatred that these men have toward women can manifest in only a couple of ways. Usually, the reason is that some women, be it their mother or some woman close to him abused them as a child in a major way. The other reason might be from birth which meant that both the mother and the father of the child carried a potent degree of the RRKD-G consequently creating a killer of man or woman.

Such a conception occurred somewhere around June or July of 1947 and as a result of said conception a little boy was born in Salt Lake City, Utah on February 18th, 1948. The boy's parents' names were Thomas and Mary Ridgway, and they named their son 'Gary Leon Ridgway'. Unfortunately for the young Ridgway boy he had to bear the brunt of his parent's dysfunction, having to grow up seeing his drunk father beat his mother on a regular basis. He Too had to take the abuse from both his alcoholic father and his demanding mother whenever she was around. That was on rare occasions because she would disappear after the beatings his father gave her, and she would stay gone for days at a time.

The angry and unpredictable behavior toward him from his mother and his father didn't help the nervous condition that young Ridgway had already developed as a child. In fact the boy would wet the bed until he was in his teens. This behavior would anger both parents and they would tease and punish him which in turn angered young Ridgeway to the point that he had thoughts of killing them. Instead at the age of 16 Ridgway took his anger out on a 6-year-old boy by stabbing him in his ribs and puncturing his liver. Fortunately the young boy survived.

Although Ridgway was tested and was shown to have an IQ in the low 80s coupled with dyslexia, he still managed to graduate from high school at the age of 19 years old. Ridgway then got married soon after that and joined the U.S. Navy that same year. After he completed his basic training the Navy sent Ridgway straight to Vietnam to serve his first years in a place where he saw little combat. During that tenure he spent a lot of time in the red-light district patronizing the local prostitutes using no protection.

After serving 18 months in Vietnam Ridgway flew back to Salt Lake City, bringing back with him the gonorrhea that hitched the flight back with him (compliments of the prostitutes). He Too promptly infected his wife who in turn promptly divorced his ass. Ridgway continued to use the services of prostitutes in Salt Lake even though he hated them.

In January of 1980 Ridgway moved to Seattle, Washington where he joined a church and after a few months met and married his second wife.

Ridgway landed a pretty good job in the Seattle, Tacoma area painting trucks and because of his and his second wife's jobs they were doing pretty well. In his spare time Ridgway would drive down to the Pacific Highway South area where prostitutes would be working and He Too would pay for their services once or twice a week. By November of 1980 women were being reported missing from that area, but the police didn't follow up on the reports because most of the women were prostitutes and/or homeless.

It wasn't until February of 1981 when a few young women were discovered near the Sea-Tac Airport in the woods close to the Green River that the police began paying attention. Thus, the Green River Task Force was formed.

For the next ten months the police and others found at least two bodies a month all young women near the Green River and the surrounding areas in King County, Washington. For the next two years young women continued to disappear, only to be found later. Some were found together in shallow graves in different parts of the woods. Seattle and Tacoma were under siege by a prolific serial killer, and the Green River Task Force assigned to the murders had no clue as to who was committing these murders.

Little did they know they had their man in the palm of their hands once. It was during their investigation that they interviewed Ridgway after he was arrested for solicitation. In 1983 He Too became a suspect in the killings but in 1984 Ridgway took and passed a lie detector test. He was slick as snot. After passing the test Ridgway became emboldened and the degree of his RRKD-G and hatred for women seemed to have elevated even higher. Shortly thereafter he went right back to killing women, hiding the bodies all over King County. He Too began returning to some of the bodies to have sex with them. The man was unhinged.

The Green River Task Force was unable to identify or capture the elusive serial killer. Four years into the hunt it got to the point when in 1984, they had to accept an offer from another serial killer to try and get some understanding of how serial killers think. That infamous serial killer was none other than Theodore Bundy, who at that time was sitting on death row for the killing spree he went on in the 1970s. Apparently, there was no Bro-Code amongst serial killers because the killer that the Green River Task Force was pursuing just so happened to be killing in the same area that Bundy frequented some years earlier. All that Bundy could do was give the Task Force his expertise and/or techniques on what he thought the killer would do next, such as the killer would probably return to a fresh kill to check on their progress or lack thereof.

Unfortunately the expert advice that Bundy gave to the officials from Washington State only served to let them know what he did to his victims, which did not apply to the Green River Killer. Even though Bundy was a well-educated serial killer in his own right, there was apparently an even more educated serial killer in Ridgway because Ridgway continued to kill several years after Bundy gave his advice. Again in 1987 the task force had Ridgway in custody and they even took saliva and hair samples from him and then released his ass again! This meant that Ridgway was again free to continue with his "career killing women," as he later called it.

It was another 14 years before the task force got around to testing the DNA samples and finally arresting Ridgway. At that time they charged him with the killings of four women that he had murdered some 20 years earlier. Why it took so long for

Washington to come up with the DNA results is a real mystery to me. Then again maybe the technology and/or testing was still in its infancy when the samples were taken from that slimy maniac. But 14 years? The GreenRiver Task Force was slipping Big Time, and while they were, Ridgway was able to murder over a dozen more women.

The four women that Ridgway left his DNA on all those years ago were young street women just trying to make a living the only way they knew how. They did not deserve to die in such a manner. Their names were as follows:

Cynthia Hinds, Marica Chapman, Carol Ann Christensen, and Opal Mills.

It is not clear as to how many women Ridgway killed after his release in 1987 until his arrest in 2001, but to avoid the death penalty he pleaded guilty to 48 murders. In December of 2003 the judge sentenced Ridgway to 48 life terms plus 480 more years for tampering with the evidence of the 48 women.

Gary Ridgway, a.k.a. The Green River Killer, was sent to the USP Florence High Federal Penitentiary in Colorado to do his life sentence.

There are several less-known and well-known individual serial rapists and serial killers that have taken many innocent lives over the years, including Jack the Ripper, Pedro Lopez, Butcher of Rostov, and John Wayne Gacy, just to name a few. What all of those men had in common was that they all possessed the primitive strain of the RRKD-G.

I just want to shed light on reasons why a man chooses to take the lives of others, men and women: One reason is for their own sick personal pleasure, and the other is that they have that out-of-control Gene.

Peonage

These days men kill for pleasure because of illness, money, out of anger, and racism, which are the main reasons. For hundreds of years killing was done for control, racism, and profit, i.e., slavery. And then when slavery, at least on paper, had run its course in this country, many White men in the Southeastern part of this country turned to committing murder. The murders came in the form of lynching, shooting, and whipping Black men to death. In fact even after slavery was abolished White men in the Southern States used what was called peonage or debt servitude to keep Black people working their coal mines and cotton fields. This practice turned out to be just as brutal if not worse than slavery itself, and it continued well after Reconstruction.

The practice of peonage accounted for thousands of deaths of Black people by being worked to death and/or just straight out murdered from 1865 to the 1940s. They died from lynchings, beatings, and simply being worked to death during that same period due to peonage. It wasn't until 1921 that this brutal practice reached the courts and the practice was discouraged. Judge John B. Hutcheson sentenced two White men for practicing peonage, murdering 11 Black men and attempting to cover it up. Those 2 White men, Clyd Manning and John Williams, both received life in prison for their involvement in the practice.

Out of the hundreds of landowners who were involved in the practice of peonage over 60 years, Manning and Williams were the first ones that were ever brought to justice. The practice of peonage continued some 20 years after the convictions of Manning and Williams by like-minded White men who possessed the vile variant of the RRKD-G. It wasn't until 1941 that Attorney

General Francis Biddle put federal prosecutors on notice that they had to bring more peonage cases to court for trial or face charges of conspiracy of the act themselves.

Here in the United States, thanks to the strict enforcement of the laws set back since the mid-1940s, peonage and debt servitude are no longer practiced. It, however, is still being practiced in one form or another in several other countries around the world to this day. The worst offenders present-day slavery and peonage are Pakistan, Russia, North Korea, and China.

Act 15: Racist White Men of Today Taking the Lives of Black Men

Walter Scott

In April 2015 a middle-aged Black man named Walter Scott was driving his car to an auto parts store in North Charleston, South Carolina to get a tail/brake light for his car. That's when Scott was pulled over by a White Charleston police officer by the name of Michael Slager.

While Slager was sitting in his cruiser running a check on Scott, Scott became nervous because he thought there might be an outstanding warrant for his arrest for back child support.

Scott had no bail money and knowing he would have to sit in jail for two or three days and lose his job he made a bad decision and decided to run from the scene. Officer Slager gave chase and somehow caught up to Scott, tackled him and then tased him. Scott was able to fight off the effects of the taser and again ran away but this time, Slager did not give chase. Instead of running back to his cruiser and calling for backup he just stood up, pulled out his service revolver and began shooting at Scott's retreating figure. Slager's aim was true; and according to the coroner Scott was hit five times, three of which were in his back.

What that White racist Slager didn't know was that all of his actions were being taped by a witness. He Too told his supervisors that he and his backup officers tried to administer CPR on Scott but the video only showed Slager planting the taser next to Scott's dying body. After the video was reviewed it was clear that Slager had no grounds to use deadly force against Scott.

After a plea deal the White racist Michael Slager was charged with second-degree murder and sentenced to 20 years in prison. Slager's decision to draw his weapon and to deliver fatal wounds to Scott's back can only be explained by the degree of his RRKD-G, which brought out the hatred of Blacks in him.

Slager should never be released from prison because chances are that he would kill again.

In October 2015 Walter Scott's family was awarded a settlement from the City of North Charleston for an amount of over six million dollars for his wrongful death.

Ahmaud Arbery

On May 8th 1994 a young Black boy was born. His parents named him Ahmaud Marquez Arbery and he grew up to be a very athletic young man. While living in Georgia jogging was just one part of Arbery's daily training. He attended Brunswick High School where he played football at a high level as a star linebacker until he graduated in 2012. Arbery then went on to attend South Georgia Technical College to further his education.

By 2020 Arbery had grown up to be a decent citizen and was loved by all who knew him. He would continue to stay in good physical condition and jogging was one of the ways he kept it even jogging 3 to 5 miles on some days. In February 2020 Arbery did as he always did, got out of bed and began his morning routine by jogging. This time it was in Glynn County, Georgia just a couple of miles from where he lived. It was not the first time that Arbery jogged in the Glynn County area but on that fateful day he caught the attention of a few racist White men.

That day of February 23rd, 2020, was unfortunate for all those involved, especially for Arbery. While he was on his run he noticed that he was being followed. After a block or two he was stopped in the middle of the street and detained at gunpoint by two racist White men, Travis and Gregory McMichael, a father and son duo. As they had Arbery standing in the street looking down the barrel of a 12-gauge shotgun another racist White man pulled up, William Bryan. Arbery had to be terrified facing those three angry White men and knowing he had done nothing wrong, he instinctively attempted to run away from that hopeless situation. As Arbery attempted to run McMichael fired at least two shots, one striking Arbery in the chest. McMichael then pulled the trigger again and struck Arbery on his wrist.

The reason for this shooting and taking the life of another young Black man was pure hatred and racism. Why do I believe that? Some people might ask. Well the fact that McMichael shot and killed an unarmed young Black man just for jogging down the street couldn't be the reason, or could it? The RRKD-G in those men caused the racist and hatred of Black people to reveal itself with deadly consequences.

Also one of a few racist texts found on Travis McMichael's phone suggested that a local restaurant, 'Cracker Barrel,' needed to change its name to 'Nigger Bucket'; this should give one a clue. The McMichaels seem to think it was alright for them to shoot and take a Black man's life because he was seen standing on private property, property that was under construction, even though the said property wasn't even theirs.

Among normal people, non-racists around this country and elsewhere in the world believe that the majority of racist people are ignorant and the rest are just plain stupid. And low and behold there came William Bryan with his stupid ass driving down the street with a camera phone in his hand, recording the very evidence that would put him and his racist friends behind bars for life.

We all know that children are taught racism and hatred and are groomed to live their lives hating others because of the color of their skin. Well at least one man, William Bryan, failed in his teachings because his daughter just so happened to have been dating a Black man while he was murdering one. So now he could sit his racist ass in that cell for the next 35 years knowing that his daughter loves a Black man and does not hate Black people.

As far as the McMichael idiots are concerned, maybe between the two of them they can spend their life sentences behind bars figuring out just when Travis was born, 1985 or 1986 because, as of right now, they don't even know.

How dumb is that?

George Perry Floyd Jr.

George Floyd was born on October 14th, 1973 in Fayetteville, North Carolina, but his parents moved to Houston, Texas, at some point in his young life, and that was where he grew up. In high school and college Floyd played both basketball and football. After leaving college he got in some trouble with the law, and after a plea bargain the judge sentenced him to four years in prison. Once he served his time Floyd began counseling the youth in his community against violence and gangs, posting his views on the internet.

Some years later Floyd relocated to St. Louis Park, Minneapolis and took on a truck driving job that lasted a few years. He then landed a security job at a nightclub in the downtown area of the city. But due to the COVID-19 pandemic that hit in early 2020, the club shut down and parts of the city closed down as well.

It was on May 25th, 2020 a beautiful spring day when Floyd and a few of his friends drove to a corner store in Minneapolis to purchase some snacks and cigarettes. While in the store one of the clerks discovered he had been passed a counterfeit $20 bill. The clerk then accused Floyd of being the one who gave it to him. The clerk's response was to call the police and it just so happened that a patrol car was only a block away from the store. The police arrived just as Floyd and his friends were getting in the car and about to leave.

The first officer on the scene was Derek Chauvin, who at that time had been with the Minneapolis Police Department for 19 years. He Too was a recipient of two medals of valor and a commendation medal for moonlighting as a security guard at a local nightclub. Over his career He Too racked up 18 complaints as well and a couple of reprimands. Chauvin was also caught on video while on a call in 2017 striking a 14-year-old Black boy in the head with his flashlight. He then pushed the boy to the ground and held him down with his knee in his back for over 16 minutes.

The clerk met Officer Chauvin in front of the store and pointed to Floyd, who was by now seated in the car with his friends. Chauvin approached Floyd and asked him for his ID. By this time two other officers had arrived on the scene and that was when Chauvin ordered Floyd out of the car and put him in handcuffs. Chauvin then proceeded to roughly escort Floyd to the police cruiser to place him in the back seat when a slight scuffle ensued.

As a result Chauvin slammed Floyd down onto the street, still handcuffed, then placed his knee on Floyd's neck. After a minute or so Floyd began complaining that he couldn't breathe, but his complaint fell on deaf ears. Chauvin continued pressing his knee on Floyd's neck even as bystanders looked on and pleaded for him to release him. Chauvin just continued kneeing Floyd on his neck and continued staring at the crowd with this stupid blank expression on his face as if he was in some trance. Onlookers were calling out to Chauvin to take his knee off Floyd's neck because he was having trouble breathing but he just continued pressing his knee on Floyd's neck. After about 8 minutes Floyd became unresponsive but Chauvin continued his pose, pressing on Floyd's neck.

The expression on his face was one that seemed as if he was enjoying ignoring the cries from the people to take his knee off Floyd's neck. Chauvin kept that pose on Floyd's neck for another minute and 46 seconds as one of the onlookers recorded it all on her camera phone.

That racist White man took the life of a Black man while being videotaped for all the world to see; he was definitely inflicted with a primitive variant of the RRKD-G.

In 2021 Derek Chauvin was tried and convicted of second-degree manslaughter, unintentional second-degree murder and third-degree murder. That racist Bastard only received a 22½ year sentence for that heinous crime. In December 2021 Chauvin pleaded guilty in a federal court for violating Floyd's civil rights and received another 21 years in prison. He Too pleaded guilty to the aforementioned act toward the 14-year-old boy, violating his civil rights as well.

These were just a few incidents from a long history of racist acts against Black men.

Act 16: Hollywood, Television, and Music

Power and Sex

During the early 1920s in Tulsa, Oklahoma White men engaged in the largest and deadliest race riot on record. In the State of Georgia, White men too engaged in the worst abuse of labor laws post-slavery, i.e., peonage and debt servitude.

But then all the way across the country on the West Coast in the 1920s in Hollywood, California, White men were involved in a different kind of labor foul play. They would continue to do so for decades to use their power and position to manipulate, and control their potential employees, and active employees to get what they wanted.

And what many of the men wanted was sexual acts to be performed by beautiful, young, and hopeful actors. These moguls of the movie industry created a method and platform that they used to get what they wanted, and it was dubbed "The Casting Couch." That term is well known to many, if not to all, women in Hollywood seeking to become the next shining star on the big screen. The women knew exactly what it meant and what was expected of them.

The powerful men heads of the studios, directors, and moguls were in full control of who would get a starring role in a movie or on television and who would just remain another struggling actress or actor in Hollywood. The cast of *characters* (pardon the pun), that felt the need to exploit the young upcoming actors or actresses reads as follows:

The first of the moguls to be exposed was the great Louis B. Mayer of the Metro-Goldwyn-Mayer Company. In 1924 Mayer was accused by Cari Beauchamp in her book of misbehaving while he was in his suite entertaining the beautiful actress   Jean Howard. In her book Beauchamp wrote that Howard told her that Mayer had chased her around the room in an attempt to engage in a sexual act of some kind with her. When he finally caught up to her and she refused his awkward advances, he vowed to take revenge on her husband, Charles K. Feldman. Mayer began doing that by not allowing Feldman or any of his clients to set foot in the MGM studio.

In another book written by Gerald Clark, titled, "The Life of Judy Garland," Clark wrote, "Mayer not only groped Garland but He Too, while she sat on his lap during an interview grabbed a handful of the then teenager's breasts."

There were other heavyweights in the industry such as Harry Cohn, Jack Warner of Warner Bros. fame, and even Ol' spooky Alfred Hitchcock. All of them were named as being less than gentlemen when they were alone with beautiful young women.

Even Marilyn Monroe, one of Hollywood's most famous and beautiful actresses, had her share of mistreatment by the powerful men of the day in that industry. She wrote in her memoir that she became disenchanted with Hollywood because of the dirty old men she had to deal with on a daily basis. She said, "I met them all; some were vicious and crooked and I had to sit there on their couches, if it were, and listen to their schemes and lies and I felt as if I was in an over-crowded brothel"

Carrie Rickey, a well-known and award-winning art and film critic grew up in Los Angeles, California, during the 1950s and later attended the University of California San Diego. She then went on to write for The New York Times, The Philadelphia Inquirer, as well as the San Francisco Chronicle. In one of her many in-your-face articles she wrote in part, "The perils of women in Hollywood are embedded like land mines," and she then went on to say, "Moguls like Harry Cohn reputedly wouldn't cast starlets like Marilyn Monroe and Kim Novak unless they auditioned in bed."

In 1962 another beautiful blond fashion model was reaching for stardom and on her path to doing so she met a famous director that thought she had what it took to become a "Star" in Hollywood. The young blonde's name was Tippi Hedren and the director that came into her life was none other than Alfred Hitchcock himself. For reasons only known to Alfred Hitchcock he thought this young actress would be the perfect fit to play the starring role in a movie about some out-of-control killer birds. Well as it turned out, Hitchcock was right again because in 1963 the movie "The Birds" was released and it became one of his greatest Big Screen Hits.

Hitchcock not only wanted Hedren on his Casting Couch for another one of his upcoming films, "Marnie," but He Too wanted to cast her in his King-Size bed with himself being the leading man.

The performance in his bedroom never took place and Hitchcock was less than pleased about her rejecting him. As a result, being the powerful director he was, Hitchcock decided that he would make things difficult for Hedren going forward, i.e., isolating her from everyone on the set.

Then there came a time when Hedren was invited to fly to New York to appear on the Tonight Show with Johnny Carson to accept an award for being "Most Promising New Star," but Hitchcock would not allow her to go. Hedren didn't say anything at the time but, in her memoir decades later she revealed that He Too sexually molested her and threatened to ruin her career if she ever told anyone. Although Hedren never spoke of the abuse until long after Hitchcock continued to place roadblocks in her acting path so her career was stymied because of his power and influence.

The aforementioned Hollywood beauties were all victims of the powerful men in the movie and film industry. Still they took their abuse like soldiers and marched on despite the shame that they kept to themselves. These few were just the ones that persevered against all odds but there were dozens of more hopeful beauties that did not survive the abuse that came with the Casting Couch.

In that era and in that business women had little or no power and in order to reach their dreams and goals they had to submit to the powers that be i.e., directors and agents. The wealthy men who preyed upon the starlets were descendants of early men who came to this country and took it. They not only took the country they also took the women they wanted as well, by force. The only difference between the men back then and the men of the 20th Century who ran the movie and film industry is that the latter didn't take the women, they just abused them. Plus they rode around in limousines and wore expensive suits instead of riding on horseback and wearing leather and animal furs as clothing.

Although the Casting Couch was widely thought to be female-exclusive the truth of the matter is that the Couch was not just for women. That was made clear in the 1940s, 50s, and beyond when an agent who went by the name of Henry Willson appeared on the Hollywood scene. Willson was well known throughout Hollywood for discovering pretty young gay boys and men, and then fine-tuning them for their appearance on television and the big screen. Willson was most famous for finding pretty much unknown actors changing their names and then turning them into well-known actors such as Guy Madison, Tab Hunter, and Rock Hudson.

All of these men went through training and transitioning in Willson's talent agency and they all too sat on Willson's Casting Couch, if you will, on their way to stardom. He Too had some young female clients that he represented, such as Ann Doran, Lana Turner, and Shirley Temple, but he preferred to work with homosexuals because that was what he was. It was no surprise to me that there were agents and or producers in Hollywood like Willson, who were bi-sexual or gay back then and even clear up to the 1970s and beyond.

Living in the Pacific Northwest in the 1970s was a very exciting and prosperous time for many. In Portland, Oregon, and Seattle, Washington, in the 1970s, both cities were full of opportunities for street-wise and business people alike. Night Clubs and Speakeasies dotted the town's landscape, leaving it wide open for the traveling live entertainers.

With that came the con men, hustlers, prostitutes, and pimps of that era, and I met many of them. The reason I was able to meet these interesting people was that I managed one of the busiest haberdasheries in Portland, Lew's Men Shop, and in the midst of all that activity, Portland, too, had its own homegrown talent.

The local and out-of-town entertainers would come to the shop where I worked and purchase outfits from me for their stage performances. There were several entertainers and hustlers that stood out to me over the years but there was one guy that I knew prsonally. I had known him for a few years and he was the lead singer in a group of four other local and talented singers from Portland. The young man went by the name Pretty Paul, which was his stage name, and he stood about 6 feet tall with a medium complexion. Women loved him and thought he was a pretty handsome guy.

Even though entertainers came through the town on a regular basis, being the small town that it was, Portland had no resident talent scouts. And there was only one music studio where groups could go and sharpen their skills or put their music on tape or wax. This meant that the local groups would have to rehearse wherever they could, in their basements or their living rooms. They would then hope that when they played at one of the clubs, there would be a promoter or talent scout from out of town who would recognize them and give them a shot.

Unfortunately there was not a lot of money to be made doing gigs at the Clubs on the weekends so the group members had to have regular jobs during the week to support their families. In Pretty Paul's case the young man had a beautiful young woman and a young child, and his woman was pregnant with their second child. Desperation was setting in.

Paul came up with this crazy idea that he could get away with robbing a bank and he figured that this was his way out of his financial situation. So with little or no planning he recruited one of his younger relatives to help him pull off this daring bank robbery in Portland, where he was pretty well known. So in the summer of 1973 Paul thought it was time to execute his not-so-well-planned bank heist. Well it turned out to be more like a comedy of errors that cost him and his sidekick dearly. Needless to say the robbery didn't turn out so well because after entering the bank and pulling out what looked like real guns but were toy guns, the two bandits got away with about $10,000.

As the pair were exiting the bank somebody recognized Paul and/or his car as they made their getaway. The two amateurs had no exit strategy so they were on the run for only a few days and the sad thing about it is that they were only 19 and 20 years old. Now they were facing 10 or 15 years in prison. After a few days had passed they were arrested and charged with armed bank robbery. After a two-week trial the jury convicted them both, and they were sentenced to seven years in prison, only because the guns were fake.

I'm not sure how Paul's side-kick spent his time while he was incarcerated or even if they went to the same prison, but I do know that Paul spent at least some of his time networking. I know this because Paul told me as much after he was released after doing three of his 7-year sentence. I didn't see Paul when he first got out of prison because he went straight from there to Hollywood, California. He went there to stay with his friend and former co-inmate. That inmate just happened to be a relative or friend of a movie producer there in Hollywood so whatever he and Paul did while in prison, his inmate friend thought Paul had what it took to become a star.

Once Paul landed at LAX his friend met him and they rode off from there in a limousine headed to a Hollywood suite where he stayed for a few weeks.

It was now the Spring of 1976 and the hit television series "Baretta" was in its second season and going strong. During Paul's stay in Hollywood his friend introduced him to one of the producers or the directors of the Baretta Show. Paul, before going to the joint, was a singer and he was comfortable singing in front of large crowds but I never knew him to take acting classes. I don't know if he took acting classes while he was in prison or not. In any case, doing whatever he did he impressed one or more of the directors of the series "Baretta" because Paul landed a small part and appeared on the show soon after.

Paul was cast as one of the bad guys on one episode of the show and when Baretta had to fight the bad guys, Paul just happened to be the one bad guy that Baretta encountered and had to hit upside the head with a beer bottle. That wack on the head knocked Paul out and that was pretty much the extent of Pretty Paul's acting career. That episode aired sometime later in 1976 and that was when Paul took his exit bow for his 15 minutes of fame in Portland for his acting debut.

I ran into Paul in 1982 several years after his appearance on the show. We met in Hawaii; he was flying in from Portland and I was flying in from Tokyo and we met just by chance at the

Honolulu Airport. We shared a limo to Waikiki where he met up with this beautiful blond dame who was the manager of a large hotel there.

But on the ride to the hotel we talked and reminisced about the times passed. I was just curious as to how he had managed to land that part on Baretta and also why he was not still in Hollywood pursuing other roles. Once we arrived at the hotel the manager put me in one of the best suites for the week I stayed there.

Later that evening we met in the hotel's restaurant and bar. We sat there laughing while we drank cognac and ate steak and lobster. We talked about everything from the bank fiasco to how he went from the Penitentiary to appearing on national television. Well he didn't go into detail about how he made it from the Pen to appearing on Baretta but he did let me know why his acting career was cut so short.

His response to this was, "Bernard, I was offered a couple of more roles but those freaks in Hollywood, i.e., the agents and directors, were just asking way too much from me. They literally wanted my ass, man! So I just stood up off that Casting Couch, left that office, and flew back home to Portland."

We then went on to have a few more drinks and powdered our noses throughout that night. We never mentioned or talked about Baretta or Hollywood again since that was the last time I saw him. That was because he and the manager of the hotel flew to another island the next day.

Sadly, my friend Pretty Paul passed away several years later, and he will be missed. God Bless his Soul.

As I mentioned earlier. I was not surprised when my research revealed that Henry Willson preferred male actors and entertainers such as Troy Donahue and Rock Hudson on his Casting Couch more so than women. The reason I was not surprised is that Pretty Paul had already made me aware of the hanky panky that was going on in Hollywood in the 70s. So I knew that 40 years earlier things had to be even more suspect. The "Casting Couch" and the men who created it go as far back as the early 1900s. Taking advantage of beautiful young women and good-looking young men was just the way things were in Hollywood and it continued into the late 1900s.

It was only during the latter when there were enough powerful women in the Entertainment Industry who decided to speak out. These women are demanding justice for past abuses, thus, The Me Too Movement.

Harvey Weinstein

One of the modern-day powerful moguls who caught the wrath of those women who were saying "Enough is enough" was the well-known Harvey Weinstein. This man had everything; he could do whatever his heart desired, he could go anywhere in the world, travel by private jet or first class, and had enough money to pay for the most beautiful women on the market.

Weinstein produced by way of his entertainment company, Miramax Films, films like The Crying Game and Sex, Lies, and Videotape. This man, Weinstein went on to win an Academy Award for producing films such as Shakespeare in Love and The Crying Game. He Too produced the hit movie Pulp Fiction. He was on a roll going on to win several Tony Awards for several other plays and musicals. This old freak couldn't keep his rich hands off all those beautiful young women who put their trust in him.

This over-sexed mogul in 2017 was accused of sexually abusing over 80 women going all the way back to the 1970s. This man not only had decades of success in producing films and plays, but He Too had gotten away with allegedly sexually abusing women for years. For years Weinstein was also allegedly obtaining sexual favors from women on the promise of furthering their movie careers, but was it eighty women? If so, just how many were sexually abused, and how many were willing participants at the time and then later just changed their minds?

Out of the eighty there were only six women, two from London, two from Los Angeles, and two from New York City, who filed criminal complaints against Weinstein, according to an article in the New York Times. In any case the man was a taker of women and he came from a generation of takers. He just happened to have been living in times when the taking of a woman was considered a crime unlike when his ancestors were taking Black slave women on a daily basis with impunity.

After several months of investigations in 2018 Weinstein had his day in court and was found guilty of rape and other sexually related felonies. Weinstein appealed the convictions but later in February 2020 he was sentenced to 23 years in prison. He Too was then extradited to Los Angeles to go to court for other related crimes.

Weinstein was not the only wealthy person who was accused of sexual misbehavior toward women and girls in the 2000s.

There are others who have a level of RRKD-G with an emphasis on sex.

William Henry Cosby Jr.

In 1965 a television series, I Spy aired on the NBC network with the stars of the show being Robert Culp and Bill Cosby. I was a 14-year-old teenager and I enjoyed watching two shows after doing my homework; they were Mission Impossible, which aired on CBS, and I Spy, which aired on NBC.

I had a hard time deciding which program I wanted to watch because both shows aired at the same time. I liked Greg Morris a Black man who starred in Mission Impossible, but I too liked Bill Cosby as well. I followed Cosby's career through the '60s and then I followed him again when he went to the Big screen. He went there in 1974 with Uptown Saturday Night, with Sidney Poitier, and then, in 1975 with Let's Do It Again, again with Sidney Poitier, The Staple Singers, and Jimmy Walker.

Bill Cosby later produced the television sitcom The Cosby Show which turned out to be one of his greatest hits running for five years on NBC. He Too, then went on to produce the spin-off "A Different World," which ran for six years. The man was on a streak! He Too produced The Cosby Mysteries, Cosby, Kids Say the Darndest Things, and Little Bill. The man was on fire!

It was in 1965 when Cosby first hit the Hollywood scene in full stride and he was like a sponge absorbing everything he could about all aspects of the business. He went from acting to directing and then eventually producing. All along the way he focused on and learned from his predecessors the ins and outs of the business, including the Casting Game.

An interesting thing about Cosby is that he was accused of sexual misconduct when he was early in his acting career but no one ever approached him. But over the last few decades Cosby had several civil sex abuse cases filed against him. There was at least one that was settled for $500,000 and at least 9 others were allegedly settled by his former insurance company, over his objections.

In 2004 14 women came forward accusing Cosby of rape and in that same year a woman a former employee of Temple University alleged that Cosby had drugged her. She then went on to say that He Too groped and digitally penetrated her while she lay in his bed helpless to fight him off.

Once she went public about what she said Cosby had done to her another woman came out and alleged that He Too drugged and assaulted her some 30 years earlier. She was an attorney practicing in California and she went on the Today Show to out Cosby for what he had allegedly done to her. Cosby has been accused by over a dozen women by this time and it seems more are coming forward at this point. All of his accusers seem to be White women.

But hold on a minute! Here came this Black Beauty, a model, actress, and singer. In 1974 she was the first African-American cover model for Vogue Magazine. This led to other American fashion designers to begin using other African-American models in their ads.

This Black Beauty said that in the mid-1980s Cosby invited her to one of his properties to discuss casting with her about appearing in one or more episodes of The Cosby Show. Later on in 2014 she wrote an article for Vanity Fair and in it she shared that on one of her visits to Cosby's Manhattan Flat he drugged a beverage he served her. She went on to say, paraphrasing, "It took me a few minutes to realize that this knucklehead had spiked my drink and before I completely succumbed to the drug I was able to call him a few choice words." Once he realized that she was on to him she wrote, "He quickly grabbed me by the arm and escorted me out the door and flagged down a taxi and threw me in it and sent me on my way."

Now if all of these women were telling the truth this meant this Cosby cat had taken what he had learned over the years about the Casting Couch Game and thrown it into warp drive. I didn't know if Black Beauty was the first Black woman that Cosby allegedly drugged but what I do know is that she is one of the finest out of those thirty-five amazing women on the cover of that magazine. And I know too that if what she said was true, Cosby must feel pretty mad at himself. Why? Because he wasn't able to close that Casting Couch deal with her as he allegedly did with all the others. When the shit hit the fan and the thirty-five women were on display on the cover of that July 2015 magazine it became clear that Cosby had a lot of explaining to do.

When I began researching the allegations that went back as far as the late 1960s I tried to make sense of the overwhelming number of accusations. I was surprised to see it was not just thirty-five but closer to sixty women had come out. I was floored. The question then became, can this be true? Just how many women were there? How many of these women were lying? How many of these women are on the money bandwagon? Then I thought to myself, was Cosby really such an idiot that felt he had to drug a dame to get laid, and not just one, but dozens?

Trying to rationalize this shit, I said to myself, "If there were thirty-five women that were willing to pose on the cover of a national magazine to say that they were victims of drugging and or rape by one man, there had to be some truth to it, right?" But then again we were not just talking about just any man; we were talking about the "Jello-Pudding Pops!" man, Bill Cosby— America's Dad!

How could this be?

Well America news flash, as bad as it might hurt or as unbelievable as it might seem, yes, it was him — Dr. Bill Cosby, who had been accused of being a serial rapist by over 50 women. Lucky for him, if true, all of these accusations were dated and dated back so far that he couldn't be prosecuted for them. Even if he committed each one of them the statute of limitation was in play in most of those cases. The question then becomes, what took these 50-plus women so long to come out with their truths about what they said Cosby did to them all those years ago?

After looking into this matter for some time I had to face the reality that even though I didn't want to believe that Mr. Cosby had committed these crimes, it wasn't looking so good for the Puddin Pop man. Plus the man himself so much as admitted to drugging at least some of the women. Cosby, for some reason, seems to have been slowly losing his moral compass. Perhaps it was just the degree of his RRKD-G that not only caused him to have allegedly committed those offenses. But it too seems to have driven him subconsciously to feel some level of guilt and caused him to incriminate himself inadvertently.

The beginning of the end for and the decline of Cosby's moral state manifested itself early in his career, the moment he thought it was alright to drug and molest women. The fact that he allegedly continued such behavior over the years with no repercussions seemed to have empowered him to believe that what he was doing was alright. For him to even have that belief points to a moral decline within his thinking. At that point Cosby may have needed immediate medical attention, which he failed to address spelling disaster for him.

Another indication that Cosby was losing his focus was that he began to disparage underprivileged young Black people. He Too went on the attack against a couple of his fellow high-powered comedians, one of whom was Eddy Murphy. In 1987 Cosby felt the need to just up and call Murphy to tell him that it was inappropriate for him to go on stage and use foul language and that he needed to stop using such profanity in his stand-up acts.

Well Murphy was at first surprised that Cosby had even called him, but he was even more surprised about why he had called. Murphy took offense to it and was so done with this knucklehead Cosby phoning him with that bullshit that he had to call his best friend. Murphy's friend was the rawest and King of stand-up, Richard Pryor. Murphy explained to Pryor what Cosby had said to him, and Pryor's response to Murphy was paraphrasing, "If that motherfucker calls you back again tell him I said, 'Suck my Dick!'" Richard didn't give a fuck about how much money Cosby had and had little to no respect for him anyway. I do know that Cosby was playing with fire when he approached Murphy about his stand-up shows because had Eddy or Richard known anything about Cosby's sexual issues at that time, they would have outed and roasted his ass way back then.

Cosby had another 18 years to pick and choose the women he allegedly wanted to drug and sexually assault. But actually the beginning of the end for Cosby was when in January of 2004 the gig was up because that was when the Temple University dame again outed him. And that was for sexually assaulting her at one of his homes in Montgomery, Pennsylvania. Later in 2005 in the deposition about her accusation Cosby said the sex was consensual. But then he admitted to giving her a drug called Benadryl. Come on Bill. Really? While in that same deposition He Too confessed to drugging young women with whom he wanted to have sex and the pills he said he gave them were called quaaludes. But He Too, long before then in 1991 he went on national television with Larry King and bragged about how he would use a drug called Spanish Fly on unsuspected women before having sex with them.

Cosby seemed to be untouchable at least for a while. That is until that determined Temple University chick continued to put the press on his ass and with the help of the World Wide Web she was able to tell her story to the masses.

But even then it wasn't until a lesser-known stand-up comedian by the name of Hannibal Buress stood on stage and rocked Bill Cosby's world by suggesting his audience go online and read what was being said about America's Dad.

Well, Buress is well-known now! I think it was only fitting that it was a young up-and-coming stand-up comedian that played such a major role in dethroning that narcissist and alleged serial womanizer and rapist in Bill Cosby. He Too, Cosby that is, had the nerve to try and give and/or pass moral judgment against Eddy Murphy and others. And this was while he was slithering around, allegedly committing the worst kind of immoral misdeeds a man could do to a woman.

While I was researching Cosby I first came to the conclusion that he allegedly turned into this serial sex offender who had it in for and was just targeting White women. Why? Maybe he just wanted to single-handedly take revenge for what the White slave masters did to Black slave girls and women during slavery. Well, that theory was somewhat debunked after he allegedly drugged that beautiful Black model.

So then I thought maybe they, Cosby and Harvey Weinstein had made a bet with each other. The bet could have probably been who would hold the record for how many women they could take from the Casting Couch to the bedroom, drug, and then rape before getting caught and charged.

If there was such a bet and I really don't believe there was one, it looked like Weinstein seems to have won it. But did he really win? Okay, Weinstein did have more accusers, close to eighty but He Too received 23 years in prison, pretty much the rest of his life. On the other hand, "Pudding Pop" Cosby was accused by only 60 women and only one took him to court. In September of 2018 he received only a 3 to 10-year sentence in state prison, plus a $25,000 fine.

After serving close to three years of that sentence in June of 2021 Cosby's conviction was overturned and he was released forthwith. So who really won? Actually there were no winners in these cases, especially for the women who said that they were abused. What good did come out of these two cases was that they allegedly exposed two of the worst sex offenders of the 20th century. Plus with the help of the brave Tarana Burke, she united dozens of women who would not have stepped forward on their own, and it gave them power, thus, the Me Too Movement.

Jeffrey Epstein

Another such person was in the news for being arrested for sexually abusing a 14-year-old girl while living in Palm Beach, Florida. This man's name was Jeffrey Epstein, a wealthy financier from Brooklyn, New York. Although he didn't have the advantage of the Casting Couch method to lure his women and girls he did have the finances to buy them. Jeffrey Epstein in 2008 served only 13 months for abusing that young girl because he had lots of money and he bought his way out.

Epstein's wealth was what allowed him to escape a lengthier prison sentence and as a result freed himself to go on and allegedly continue to commit even more sexual assaults against girls and women. In fact in 2019 Epstein was again arrested on federal charges for sex trafficking of teenagers in New York and Florida.

Epstein began his path to wealth by becoming a financial adviser to a billionaire client by the name of Leslie Wexner in 1986. In a year's duration Epstein was able to straighten out Wexner's entangled financial problems and by 1991 Epstein had earned the trust of Wexner so much so that Wexner signed over power of attorney to him. This meant that Epstein could buy and sell properties, borrow money, and sign checks on behalf of Wexner.

This promotion put Epstein on the fast track and by 1995 he rose to be the Director of the Wexner Foundation and President of Wexner's Property, which made him a multi-millionaire. Epstein, now that he was a rich man could begin rubbing shoulders and mingling with and befriending other wealthy people such as Donald Trump, Alan Dershowitz, and even Prince Andrew, aka The Duke of York, to name a few. But perhaps the closest friend and sometimes lover Epstein had was Ghislaine Maxwell, a well-educated socialite from France. Maxwell, too, was a woman with friends in high places and was also a close friend of Prince Andrew. And as it turned out Maxwell and Epstein became partners in crime for over 20 years. It had been said that Maxwell would allegedly, from time to time go out and find and hire young girls to come back with her to Epstein's properties to entertain him.

Epstein owned several properties throughout the state. He Too owned a private island where he would invite his wealthiest friends and fly young girls and women there to keep them company, if you will. In 2011 Epstein was tagged as a high-risk sex offender in New York State and was ordered to report to the New York Police Department every 90 days.

In 2014 a young quasi-prostitute claimed that Epstein and Maxwell had trafficked her when she was 17 years old, along with other underage prostitutes, for their personal pleasure. She also stated that she was Epstein's sex slave for almost three years and that he introduced her to a few of his wealthy friends as well.

She even named a couple of the friends, one of which was Prince Andrew himself, and she appeared in a photo hugging the Prince while they were on Eptsein's private island. Her cries for someone to believe her story and help her get the justice she so sought paid off after several years. She led the way for the 2019 arrest of Epstein for the sex trafficking of minors in New York, but unfortunately she never saw him in court.

Epstein was in jail from the time he was arrested in July, awaiting trial but on the 10th of August 2019 he was found dead in his cell. Some said it was suicide, while others were not so sure. Before his death Epstein settled several out-of-court lawsuits pertaining to the sex trafficking of minors.

I really don't know why Epstein felt the need to take his own life if, indeed that is what he did. I say that because I believe he had a chance to minimize his jail time had he fought that case. Because he didn't rape anybody he just paid teenage prostitutes for their time, something that goes on in this country every day. There is something very fishy about Ebstein's suicide claim.

I think the age of consent in this country is the highest worldwide. In Germany, the age of consent is 14; in Canada, it is 16; and in Japan, it is 13, and guess what? In Nevada, it's 16, and in New York, it is 17.

Now that Epstein was dead the quasi-prostitute that accused him of abusing her, along with her attorney set their sights on Maxwell and Prince Andrew. In July 2020 the F.B.I. arrested Maxwell in Branford, New Hampshire, for sex trafficking of minors. In December of 2021 18 months after her arrest Maxwell was convicted of said sex trafficking charges and is now facing 60-plus years in prison.

On January 29th, 2022 Ghislain Noelle Marian Maxwell was sentenced to 20 years in prison for her involvement in sex trafficking, which I think was excessive. All the woman may have been guilty of was introducing beautiful young girls to wealthy clients so they could make more money, instead of standing on the street corners. But Maxwell's problem was that some of the girls were only 14 years old, but in her defense the girls continued to return for more, for years, on their own. Did they give her 20 years for just that? Had Maxwell practiced her ventures in Japan, she would still be a free woman today.

The one young lady who started all of this was pleased with Maxwell's arrest and conviction, but she was not yet satisfied; she now wanted Prince Andrew to pay. She wanted to get paid much more than what she had already gotten from him or Epstein for the services she gave to the Prince when she was a teenager.

For several years and even appearing on national television in 2019 the Prince denied and claimed he had no recollection of ever meeting the woman. Then when that photo appeared in 2001 of him, her, and Maxwell all standing together in plain sight at that event, he still said he didn't recall that meeting.

But in a strange turn of events several months later in February of 2022 Prince Andrew agreed to an out-of-court settlement with the said woman for an undisclosed amount. He

Too agreed to make a large donation to the woman's favorite charity to support victim's rights.

So in the end this former young quasi-prostitute single-handedly brought down one multi-millionaire, a rich socialite, for trafficking in the oldest profession known to man: prostitution. She too in the process exposed the Duke or Prince of the British Royal Family as being one of her wealthiest clients.

And if that wasn't enough she too inspired thousands of young prostitutes around the world, as inadvertently as it may have been, never to give up because they too could land a millionaire or a Royal for a client.

Not since Edward Lewis, played by Richard Gere in the 1990's romance/comedy Pretty Woman, had any man paid a quasi-hooker so much money for sex.

Unlike in the movie the Prince not only didn't marry the hooker, he says he didn't even remember meeting her. Yeah, right, Prince. I bet he remembers her ass now.

It is noteworthy to mention that the activity Epstein chose to embark on in his spare time as a sexual predator of under-aged girls was as low and as foul as a man could go.

But then for him to have found a woman who could agree with and participate in such behavior with him, Maxwell, was remarkable. I can only contribute their behavior to the fact that they both were suffering from a variant of the RRKD-G with emphasis on sex. Together, they were like gasoline and fire.

After all that was said and done in this year's long violation of young girls, there were others—dozens of them who were awarded monies ranging in hundreds of thousands. And a few were awarded monies in multi-millions. Hopefully those awards will ease some of their pain.

Robert Sylvester Kelly

Another bright and talented Black man allowed his fame and fortune to fool him into believing that he could really fly and fly high enough that he could escape reality and responsibility for his unusual activities. Robert S. Kelly was born on January 8th, 1967 on the South Side of Chicago, Illinois, to a single mom because his father never stepped up to guide him. In an autobiography written in 2012 Kelly admits to being sexually abused by an older female member of his family at an early age.

He Too went on to write that at the early age of 10, he was sexually abused by an older male figure as well, and when asked why he never told anyone he wrote, "I was too ashamed." In 1980 at the age of 13, Kelly was enrolled in Kenwood Academy a 4-year High School where he began playing basketball at a high enough level that the coach put him on the team. As it turned out basketball became Kelly's first love and he excelled at it, becoming one of the star players on the team. Kelly later enrolled in the music class where he met a music teacher at Kenwood who took an interest in his talent.

After a few classes the music teacher's ears focused on Kelly's voice and she was captured by what she heard. She wanted more. After a few weeks of fine-tuning Kelly's voice she convinced him to perform in the High School's Talent Show where he went on to win the first prize. On receiving a standing ovation from the audience Kelly was convinced that singing was his future. After a few more basketball games and with the music teacher's encouragement Kelly quit the basketball team and set his sights on his music.

Kelly after only one year at Kenwood dropped out due to a learning disability, dyslexia which prevented him from excelling in reading and writing. Kelly continued both singing and playing basketball, singing in the subways of Chicago and balling with his best friend, the late Ben Wilson. Wilson was one of Illinois State's Champion Basketball players. After Wilson was shot and killed in 1984 Kelly sang at his funeral and the song he sang was "It's So Hard to Say Goodbye to Yesterday," written by Freddie Perren and Christine Yarian in 1975.

For the next five years Kelly worked hard on his singing skills teaming up with other talented up-and-coming singers like Shawn Brooks, Vincent Walker, and Marc McWilliams. In 1989 they went to MGM and presented the company with a song called "Why You Wanna Play Me." MGM recorded the tune and released it in 1990 but it didn't go very far, nor did the group. They broke up shortly afterwards.

In 1991 Kelly and a group called Public Announcement collaborated and they went on tour in 1993 but that too was short-lived but profitable. Together they produced the album "Born Into the 90's", which stayed on the R&B charts for nine straight weeks.

Kelly left the group in that same year and went on to break out with his first solo album, 12 Play and the first number-one hit on the album was "Bump N' Grind," which stayed on the Billboard Hot R&B Singles chart for 12 weeks. R. Kelly continued singing, writing, and producing and in 1994 two of his singles, "Sex Me" and "Your Body's Callin," both sold over 500,000 copies in the United States alone. In a couple of years "12 Play" ended up becoming a 6-time platinum album. Kelly was on a feverish roll and in 1995 he was nominated for two Grammys for writing, composing, and producing "You Are Not Alone," a song by Michael Jackson released that same year.

Kelly not only continued writing and composing his own hits, He Too wrote for other artists and the remarkable thing about it is that R. Kelly was diagnosed with dyslexia. That so-called disability was supposed to have prevented Kelly from being able to read or write, but somehow, he learned how to do both, which speaks to how intelligent he really was. Kelly's rise up the R&B charts did not go unnoticed. In fact in 1995 he was being compared to Soul artists such as Marvin Gaye, Barry White, and Donny Hathaway. The man was on fire. In 1995 and 96 Kelly released several gold and platinum albums; the most popular single was released in November of 1996, titled "I Believe I Can Fly," reaching No.2 on the Billboard Hot 100 and No.1 in the UK.

Kelly never lost his passion for his first love which was basketball. In between writing hit records for himself and others Kelly decided in 1997 to just up and try out for a professional basketball team. Who does that? Kelly not only tried out for the team but He Too made the team. It wasn't the NBA but it was a professional basketball team. It was the Atlantic City Seagulls who signed Kelly to a contract. I guess by joining the team he was proving to everyone that he could indeed fly, at least that he could fly to the hoop.

This brilliant songwriter and producer continued to thrive and dazzle his fans over the years with his music adding award after award to his resume. The man was truly metaphorically, flying high in his career.

During his recording career Kelly put his stamp on and worked with some of the most talented artists in the industry. He touched on artists such as Mary J. Blige, Jenifer Hudson, Lady Gaga, Mariah Carey, Celine Dion, Lil Wayne, Justin Bieber, and the list goes on. Kelly had arguably taken the title of The Hardest Working Man in Show Biz from the amazing and legendary James Brown.

When a male entertainer the caliber of R. Kelly is on a roll he develops a following and in that following He Too becomes somewhat of a sex symbol. The groupies came out of the woodwork and were everywhere, in and out of this country. The numbers were in the thousands, mostly young females, but even the more mature women became mesmerized by the charisma and Kelly had it all at one time in his career: money and power.

While Kelly was flying high in the 2000s hovering just below him were the acts that he had done and the acts that he had allegedly done in the 1990s. One such act took place in 1991 when a young girl named Tiffany, age 15 alleged that she and Kelly engaged in sexual activities on a few occasions. The sex acts included threesomes with a few other of his underaged girlfriends. Before this activity became public knowledge Kelly allegedly settled a lawsuit with the girl's parents for the sum of $250,000.

In 1992 there was a young up-and-coming singer from Detroit who went by the name Aaliyah. Her then-manager introduced her to R. Kelly at the tender age of 12 years old. Over the next year or so Kelly and Aaliyah were in and out of the studio working on songs. By May of 1994 Kelly had written, produced, and recorded Aaliyah's first album 'Age Ain't Nothing but a Number,' which became certified double platinum, selling over 3 million copies here in the United States and 6 million copies around the world.

As it turned out Kelly and Aaliyah were not only making music in the studio He too was making music with her in his bedroom, and in August of 1994 the duo got married (Wife #1). She was just 15 or 16 and he was 27. The marriage only lasted six months and it was annulled in February 1995. Kelly again allegedly, paid another $250,000 to a male member of Aaliyah's family.

The money was a settlement for him to keep quiet about what he knew about the details of the illegal marriage. By this time Kelly was a rich man and had flocks of women, young and old, chasing after him and his money but Kelly preferred to have younger women, much younger.

It was not a far stretch to assume that the reason Kelly was drawn to younger women or teenage girls was that an older woman sexually abused him as a youth.

It would be remiss of me not to mention and give a heartfelt shout-out to the late, great, and talented Aaliyah, who tragically died in a plane crash way too soon in 2001. May she rest in peace!

In 1997 R. Kelly was in Atlanta, Georgia doing a video shoot for his Home Alone project and this beautiful young Coco complexed Black woman walked in and caught his eye. Kelly had his cousin reach out to snag her and bring her to him. I'll just call her Girl 2 because Aaliyah was Girl & Wife1. Girl 2 was just 17 years old but pretty much out on her own. After a bit of small talk Kelly wasted no time. He had to have her.

He allegedly invited her to fly out to Chicago for a visit, and she called him a month later and accepted his invitation. Kelly then allegedly had one of his people send Girl 2 money to get her ID and enough for a first-class plane ticket to Chicago. Once she arrived at the airport there was a limo waiting for her. She was then driven straight to Kelly's studio where he was there to greet her.

Kelly made sure she was very comfortable there in the studio. She had her own very nice bedroom right there in the studio. Whatever happened on that visit in Chicago Girl 2 wanted more because he flew her back home after a couple of weeks. In less than two weeks she was right back there in Chicago at the studio with Kelly. It is unclear as to what Girl 2's sex life was before she met Kelly but she had no problem going all out to please her new man. Before she knew it Kelly allegedly had her joining him in sex acts that included other underage girls in threesomes. Now the threesomes in and of themselves are no big deal. Women do it all the time to please their men or even themselves; that was not the problem. Girl 2's problem was three-fold: first, it was the frequency in which Kelly demanded them; second, it was that Kelly allegedly wanted her to have them with underaged girls, I mean real under. And if that wasn't kinky enough He Too had to christen the ongoing acts, not with Champagne but by pissing on the girls in real-time. The question now is, why would Girl 2 stay in that relationship after seeing Kelly doing his pissing act? Her answer to that question was: "Well he asked me if it was alright for him to piss on me and I told him no, and the issue never came up again."

The fact of the matter is Girl 2 was lost and turned out because she stayed with Kelly for a few years afterwards. But then again women piss on men all the time during sex, and they call it *squirting* (Google it), so what? Is there a double standard at play here? Kelly's money allowed him to glide above those scandals and he continued to produce hit after hit for years. But in February of 2002 a video was sent to the Chicago Sun-Times that allegedly showed Kelly having sex with and pissing on another underage girl. Kelly's defense when asked about the video was simple: "It Wasn't Me." I know Kelly said that he was sexually abused as a child but I don't remember him mentioning that the older woman had pissed on him.

So if that was indeed him on the video I don't know where he learned the act of pissing on a woman. But what I do believe is that the trauma of Kelly's sexual violation as a child was enough to trigger the RRKD-G within him and he began taking his anger and rage out on women, young and old. Apparently the authorities didn't believe Kelly's denial that he was not the figure in the video either because in June 2002 Kelly was indicted and later arrested on 21 counts of child pornography. Shortly after that he was released on a $750,000 bond but later the case was dismissed because the victim would not testify.

Later during a search of Kelly's home in Davenport, Florida, police came across 12 more images of the same young woman that was seen being pissed on in the first video in a camera they found in the home. Kelly was again arrested a few months later and charged with 12 counts of possession of child porn and he made bail of $12,000 for those charges. It seemed as though Kelly was headed for a crash landing but in 2004 those charges were dropped due to lack of evidence as well. For the next five years or so there was little or no turbulence in Kelly's life. It seemed as though he was flying straight up until 2009 when he was accused of molesting another teenage girl.

Three years later Kelly met a young lady whom I will call Lady #1. Lady#1 said in a BBC news article that after dating Kelly for a couple of years she flew to Johns Creek, Georgia, to live with Kelly at his home there. She said the only thing about it was that He Too had a few of his other underaged girls living there and that he controlled them all with an iron fist. Kelly was a man who liked young girls or women. That is no secret he even admits to it. Once Lady #1 realized that she was not the only woman there, she was ready to bounce knowing a teenager she was not. She was well in her 30s. She stayed in his home in Georgia with girls half her age and according to her she was forced by Kelly to have threesomes with a couple of them.

Not only that, she says she took lots of Kelly's verbal and mental abuse for a few weeks until she couldn't take it anymore. She caught a flight back home with a broken heart and a life lesson. She should have known that she was too old to be chasing after a player like R. Kelly, trying to compete with teenage beauties...

In 2011 Kelly performed a concert outside Dallas, Texas and after the concert he and his entourage went to a well-known after-hours Club in Mansfield, Texas called, Fat Daddy's. That was where he met this Black beauty whom I'll just call Lady #2, and although she was a more seasoned woman than he preferred, Kelly was captured. According to Lady #2, Kelly gave her his number and after they kicked it for a while she left there with a smile on her face.

Lady #2 had finally met the man she had been fantasizing about for years. Well she no longer had to pretend anymore, she was now involved in the real world of R. Kelly. This encounter turned out to be a classic case of 'be careful of what you wish for.'

Lady #2 knew about Kelly and what he had been accused of doing over the years pertaining to underaged girls. However, she was so mesmerized that she didn't want to believe any of what she read, heard, or saw. She knew about the sex tape that was shown throughout the United States, alleging that it was R. Kelly pissing on a teenager. She too knew Kelly was indicted for that and several other porno acts, which clearly should have been red flags, but not to her. According to Lady #2, she quit her good-paying job as a DJ at a Dallas, Texas radio station in 2012 to go and live with Kelly in Chicago.

Well, Lady #2 was now living in Kelly's home with a few other much younger beauties and then the games began. She stayed in the house for a few months and then Kelly allegedly moved her into his studio with two other underage girls. And yes, they all had separate rooms. He Too allegedly took their phones away so they couldn't call friends or family without his permission. Lady #2 claims that Kelly would starve her, sometimes for a day or two before ordering food for her to eat. According to her, whenever Kelly got the notion he would call out one or two of the young girls to a playroom in the studio and force her to have sex with them while he taped it. She also said she witnessed Kelly pissing on the girls while they were engaged in sex acts.

This woman was now front and center finding herself involved in performing sex acts with those young girls and R. Kelly himself. This was the very thing she heard and talked about on her radio station, saw on television, and read in the newspapers years earlier. She stayed with Kelly for several more months, continuing to perform sexual acts with those girls. Why? Kelly must have just brought out the freak in her and she took some pleasure in it. She was a grown-ass woman and knew how to open that door and get her little hot ass out. She was not this scared little 16-year-old child.

The aforementioned girls and women are just a few of Robert Kelly's accusers; there are several more that were not mentioned. But with their combined testimonies a federal jury in Brooklyn, New York, was able to convict Kelly on nine counts of racketeering and sex trafficking. Leading up to the conviction of Robert Kelly there were at least a half dozen new women who went on record by appearing on a television show claiming Kelly had sexually abused them in some way. There too were a couple of women who spoke against Kelly on that show and yet did not accuse him of sexually violating them.

The first of those two women was his wife, Wife #2. She spoke against Kelly after years of withholding her judgment of him after hearing about all of the accusations of his misconduct towards the then girls and women. It wasn't until the sex tape appeared that showed her husband allegedly having an inappropriate sex act with a minor that she was convinced of his guilt. She, of all people, knew what her husband's body looked like and after seeing it on that video, it was a wrap. As hurtful as it was to her to come to that realization she didn't want to, but she expressed the pain she felt, not just for herself but for her children as well. Because she knew that they were about to face shame for what their father had done, her last words for Kelly were, paraphrasing, "For the shame you brought to and on us, you can go straight to hell!"

The other woman who had not been sexually abused by Kelly but spoke out against him was this voluptuous high-yellow dame who collaborated with Kelly to produce her debut album.

I'll just refer to her as Lady #4. She spoke against Kelly on a couple of appearances, once on the T.V. show "Surviving R. Kelly" and another on a Chicago radio station. She spoke out because she was convinced that the young girl in the sex video with whom many thought was R. Kelly was a 14-year-old close relative. The question then becomes, you may be sure that the girl on the video is your relative, but why are you so sure that R. Kelly is the man pissing on her?

Well one reason could be that Kelly allegedly agreed to produce Lady #4's debut album after one of his staff presented him with a demo that she and her significant other had recorded. Kelly heard it and seemed to like it. He then allegedly told his staff member to tell Lady #4 that he would produce her album on one condition. That condition would be that she, and she alone would have to come to live and sleep on the couch (Kelly's version of the Casting Couch) at the studio. She would have to stay there for the 30 days it would take to complete the album. Lady #4 allegedly agreed and that meant that she and Kelly had a lot of alone time in the studio, the studio that had a few bedrooms.

When asked during an interview on the Chicago radio station if she and Kelly ever hooked up sexually, the first thing to come out of her mouth wasn't 'no,' it was like, "Well, he liked me, and Robert is or was a handsome guy, but we were more like family." That answer didn't seem totally convincing to me. I'm just saying.

Seeing her and listening to her, Lady #4 didn't come off to me as being this dumb blonde. Being around and spending time with Kelly knowing that he was signing all of those $200,000-plus (be quiet) checks for other girls, and knowing that He Too was lusting for her, I don't know if she was able to resist his advances and wealth.

Just a little footnote: Lady #4 allegedly never did go back to her significant other after spending those 30 days with R. Kelly.

Hmmmm!

Robert Sylvester Kelly was born with an ultra-raw talent that when unleashed allowed him to soar to the top of the entertainment Game, reaching ultimate success and wealth. His success spread over decades and his music reached around the globe touching millions of lives. Sadly Kelly on the inside was battling with personal demons that wouldn't allow him to do as much good for people and or causes he would have chosen to bless. Ironically Kelly's staunchest supporters, the ones that loved him the most were the ones that he let down and hurt the most: Women!

R. Kelly's spectacular rise to wealth and fame was eclipsed only by his equally spectacular subsequent disgraceful fall. He was able to entertain and excite girls and women around the world. He Too, over the years managed to transform himself from being an American Idol into being one of the most vulgar and vile individuals that ever set foot on a stage.

R. Kelly's fall from grace was inevitable because although he was able to practically swoon and swoop women off their feet with his crooning and salacious stage performances, he could not continue to hide his true feelings for women.

Evidence of that manifested itself over the years with the complaints of sexual abuse and other mistreatments toward several women. Kelly's efforts to conceal his feelings of dislike for the women who so loved him failed. The ugly truth revealed itself. He not only disliked women, but He Too took from some of them   their dignity. He Too just had to piss on some of them to make his feelings clear. R. Kelly in 2019 was convicted of eight counts of transporting people across the State-lines for prostitution and was held without bond for close to two years while awaiting sentencing.

Well in late June 2022 Robert S. Kelly was sentenced to thirty years in prison for what the jury said he did.

I don't believe Kelly is guilty of that because he is not and has never been a pimp. Kelly just happened to like young girls and they liked him too. Some of them were at the age of consent, and some were not. Kelly was guilty of having sex with and pissing on young girls and women. Is that a jailable offense? Again, as was mentioned earlier women and girls piss on men all the time during sex: it's called squirting. Should they be charged for pissing on men?

Unfortunately for Kelly a few months later another jury in Chicago found him guilty as well, which meant he would be receiving even more time in prison.

Sad but true story.

Act-17: The Clergy

While researching laymen for their alleged sexual abuses, be it a child or woman of age as the victim. I couldn't help but notice how nowadays the prosecutors go really hard after a perpetrator, even if the case is a cold one. I believe that all sex offenders and rapists should be held accountable for their misdeeds. I want to throw a few names out there in order to make some comparisons about how the following people were treated as opposed to the laymen who were charged in similar cases.

First, there is Priest Mauricio Viquez, who was dismissed from the University of Costa Rica for the rape of several young boys, and He Too was found guilty and sentenced to 20 years. Viquez is currently on the run.

Then we have Priest James Talbot, who was sentenced to and served six years in prison for sexually abusing several students at Boston College High School. He Too transferred to Maine, where he taught and molested several other boys in a Jesuit school. The victims sued the School and the Society of Jesus and received $5.2 million. No one knows where Talbot is today.

Another such case involves a Catholic Priest from Cincinnati, Geo Drew, who instead of going to trial and facing a 99-year sentence for raping a couple of young boys at St. Jude School in Green Township, Ohio, he decided to take a plea that allowed him to do only seven years. No one knows where he is today either.

What is shocking is that sexual abuse of children by priests has been going on not just in the United States but around the world for decades. A case in point:

The Catholic news agency CNA in Germany had claimed that they discovered copies of the court's decision pertaining to the sexual abuse of several children by clergy members during the 1960s and 1970s. It was reported that the main perpetrator was Bishop Rudolf Motzenbacker, who is now deceased.

But it was said that He Too had nuns bring some of his victims to him at his apartment and he would pay the nuns for doing so. One of the men who broke the story at the time was an altar boy and victim of Motzenbacker and the diocese paid him $18,000 for what he went through for those years. Whoever that young man was I just want to say to him that the church not only allowed the priest to rape you, but they also insulted you by offering you such a minimal amount of compensation for such a major criminal violation. Who are these people?!

Now let us be clear: we are now talking about priests here— the servants of God in the Church committing sexual acts against the youth of the Church, boys and girls.

Way over in India the beat goes on. There we have a 52-year-old Catholic Priest by the name of, Robin Vadakkumchery who was accused, tried, and convicted of raping and impregnating a 16-year-old student that was attending the Church-backed School in Kannur, a city in Kerala, India.

The Courts found Vadakkumuchery guilty of three charges brought against him and at first sentenced him to 60 years but later reduced it to 20 years.

He Too was denied a request to the Supreme Court to allow him bail so that he could marry the child that he raped and impregnated. The Priest had some balls–pardon the pun.

I can go on and fill up 5 or 6 pages with names of all of the Priests who have committed sexual acts against underage children, some of whom were girls but mostly young boys. The astonishing thing about this issue is the number of Priests who have been accused of sexually abusing so many children, in so many places, for so many years. From 2001 all the way to 2010, the Apostolic saw itself being investigated for sex abuse cases involving nearly 3,000 Priests, some cases going as far back as 50 years. My question is: "How did all of these men ever become Priests in the first place, who hired them, and what screening did they have to go through to become Priests? There are more questions than answers. Another question is: "How did these pedophiles know that by joining the church there would be this array of young boys and girls for them to prey upon?

An Austrian Cardinal, Hans Hermann Groer stepped down from his position as Archbishop of Vienna because he allegedly abused a few boys. Furthermore research revealed that since 1995 there have been more than 100 Priests convicted of sexual abuse in Australia.

This sort of behavior by the Clergy has been highlighted and received media attention since the 1990s, and payoffs and settlements have been issued to many of the victims. The reality is that Catholic Priests have been knocking boots on young under-aged girls and sodomizing young boys going as far back as the 15th century when Pope Leo X was head of the Church.

The fact of the matter is clear: Those Clergymen are nothing but pedophiles draped in Religious garments. All of those men have or had a variant of the RRKD-G that drove them to target and rape young boys and girls for their sexual pleasure. Members of the Catholic Church, high and low men and women, all knew about what was going on but simply kept quiet. What does that say about the Pope and his not-so merry men that are running the Churches?

There is nothing worse than an adult sexually violating a minor child, be it a boy or girl. And whoever engages in such practices should be prosecuted to the full extent of the law, especially the so-called men of God.

Act-18: Boy Scouts of America Organization—The Touchy Feelers

Man during his time on this planet has accomplished and performed extraordinary feats. Still, He Too has experienced colossal failures through the millenniums as well and that is because man is an imperfect being. There are close to 8 billion people on this earth in 2022 and arguably, 50% are male.

All humans possess the RRKD-G but only a fraction grow up to be killers and or rapists. There are 330 million people living in the United States, according to the 2020 census.

In 2022 the Boy Scouts of America (BSA) youth organization at the last count had 2.3 million youth members. The organization today has close to 890,000 adult volunteers, 97% of whom are White people who were and now are running and looking after these Boy Scouts. That number 2.3 is less than half of what it was in 1979. It is astonishing to see a significant number of individuals still involved today considering the troubling allegations that have surfaced regarding the organization's history.

What was it that the BSA allowed to happen you might ask? Well, during the years leading up to 1994, there were around 2000 cases of sexual abuse allegations against this organization.

This means that over the years millions of families entrusted their young boys to this organization thinking that their loved ones would be taken care of and they would be safe. Wrong! Even more disturbing is that there were 92,000 sexual abuse claims filed in the courts prior to and leading up to the end of 2020.

A Boy Scout who was abused in the 1980s was in 2010 awarded the largest-ever settlement against the BSA to date and the courts awarded the man $18.5 million. Therein lies the question: Just how many of those 890,000 volunteers were involved in the sexual abuse of all of those boys, and how were they allowed to continue doing so to so many boys? So what is being said is that there were at least a hundred sexual child predators working in the BSA organization. Is that for real?

Okay, I'm not a mathematician and I had trouble with long division in school, but even I know it takes more than one sexual predator to commit 92,000 abuses. Who are these people and just how many pedophiles does it take to commit 92,000 abuses? I know too that there are sexual predators in all nationalities but you White men have taken this child sexual abuse of boys to another dimension.

Between the Boy Scout volunteers and the Catholic Priest the violations of young boys spiked well over 150,000 cases in the last 20 years, out of which 99% were committed by White men. The abuse of young boys by White men can only be attributed to the strain of the RRKD-G in White men, which is a sub-variant rarely found in any other nationality.

Catholic Church and Georgetown University: Jesuit Priest

Another issue I have is with the Catholic Church and in particular, its Jesuit Priests, as if abusing young boys from behind and sucking on them wasn't enough. Is there a greater heinous crime against humanity? Because how low can one stoop?

Well just as the brilliant Henry Louis Gates Jr. always does he uncovered another low and disturbing fact about the Jesuit Priests who migrated to this country in the 1630s and he needs to be commended for doing so. He Too discovered that the Jesuits came from somewhere in Europe to escape persecution and landed here in the Northeastern portion of what is now the United States. The congregation ended up in several towns and or states surrounding the Washington D.C. area and began farming throughout. Over time the Jesuit Priests purchased over 13 thousand acres of farmland where they grew tobacco and other crops.

It is not clear as to which one of those early Jesuit Priests came up with that great idea to buy and enslave Black men and women to work and cultivate all of those acres of land they purchased. Neither is it clear as to what year the first slaves were purchased   or even how many were purchased. Estimates ranged from 30 in 1700 and by 1730 the Jesuit Priests owned close to 150 slaves and they used those slaves to maintain and grow their massive crops and tobacco fields.

They not only used the slaves as farm laborers   but they were also used to lay the foundations for housing and other buildings along the banks of the Potomac River. What is known by only a few but needs to be known by many is that not only was slave labor used to set the foundations but it was also used to build those dwellings as well. The most significant and largest building among those is Georgetown University in Northwest Washington, standing there in all of its glory. The Georgetown

College or University was completed in 1789 and at that time the Jesuit Priests owned a staggering 300 plus slaves working them day and night in and around the campus and elsewhere. Georgetown University was up and running for the better part of 50 years but running as it may, the administrators dropped the ball. They ignored their financial responsibilities for many of those years as well. With their back against the wall due to the mismanagement of company funds, the powers that be of Georgetown had to come up with monies to pay off the huge debts that they had accumulated over the years. So in 1838 again the brilliant minds at Georgetown spearheaded by Thomas Mulledy, the acting Jesuit president decided to sell 272 of the 320 Black slaves they owned in order to cover their debts.

With the blessing of the Catholic Church in Rome the Jesuit Priests here transferred the 272 slaves to ships and loaded them on bound for plantations in the South as far away as Georgia and Louisiana. The sale of those slaves was the largest human transaction for profit ever in this country. The Jesuit Priest sold the 272 slaves for $115,000, which in today's money would be close to $3 million.

Here again we have White men demonstrating their hatred for Black people even though they themselves barely escaped from persecution. They came here to America only to become persecutors of another nationality under the auspices of the Roman Catholic Church. Go figure!

The sale of those 272 Black slaves by the Georgetown Priest was swept under the rug for over a hundred years. It's only been ten years or so since the issue of the atrocity committed by

Georgetown University has come to light and the present-day students have organized protests and sit-ins.

The students demanded that the names of the presidents, Rev. William McSherry and Rev. Thomas F. Mulledy, involved in the sale of the 272 Black slaves, be removed from around the Campus Buildings and elsewhere.

After some resistance from the administration the University compiled. And not only that a Georgetown alumnus, Richard Cellini stepped up. What he did was hire several genealogists to investigate and track down descendants of as many of the slaves as possible. Mr. Cellini a member of the Catholic Church and Dr. Adam Rothman, a Georgetown historian is proof positive that the primitive strain of the RRKD-G is continually being diluted.

This too means that there is still hope for the human race. This is true because those two White men truly believe that what Georgetown University and other Universities engaged in - the Slave Trade -was unjust and atrocious and they all need to make amends and be held accountable.

Epilogue

The point I've been attempting to make in these writings, if there are those who don't quite get it, is that men for thousands of years have believed that they were put on earth to take from others, whatever they want. Men have taken property, land, and even other people, women in particular. Depending on what your beliefs are, whether it be believing in God or whether you believe in Evolution, either way the beginning of man's journey and throughout history has been riddled with violence. If it's religion you favor then one has to face the fact that in the beginning in the Garden or in an area nearby there was jealousy, violence, and even murder between brothers.

Now if you are one of those who lean towards the Theory of Evolution, there too is evidence of violence, murder, and even cannibalism among early men. So it should be noted that man is an imperfect being and even after all of these centuries he still hasn't gotten it completely right.

Women throughout history have always had power but only a few women in Ancient History took advantage of their power. Modern-day women just didn't know the power they had and it took thousands of lifetimes before they figured it out. It wasn't until the late 20th Century that women began exercising their true power and it felt good to them.

Women had power right there in the palms of their hands—well, not exactly in their hands, but in their brains and between their legs. That reality came to light in this country in the mid-1900s when White women noticed that their husbands, their fathers, and their brothers were no longer able to take and rape Black women at will without consequences.

White women then realized that times had changed and all of a sudden they began seeing more of their husbands in their own bedrooms. And they too noticed fewer pregnant Black slave women walking around carrying their husbands' children.

It still took another 100 years for White and Black women to finally speak to their power and call out and expose the injustice that they have so long had to endure. And it's only fitting that it took a strong Black woman, Tarana Burke to have spearheaded and exposed the men that controlled the status quo,

(The Me Too Movement)

. What a difference a hundred-plus years makes! But it would have been better if White women back then had used their untapped powers to help free Black women. The suffering inflicted on Black women by their White men, their husbands, their fathers, and their brothers would have ended a long time ago.

Ever since the beginning when the White man figured out how to build ships and sail the oceans he displayed his cruelty, barbarism, and brutality. It was he who sailed to Africa kidnapping Black people to enslave them. It had never been said that Black men from Africa built ships and sailed anywhere to kidnap White people to enslave them. The White man mastered the art of importing Black people from Africa to the Americas to build this country into what it is today and they had been living for centuries off of the backs of Black slaves.

But let us be clear: I'm not at all saying that the end justifies the means because it has been a very violent and turbulent journey to get to where we are today.

As recent as the 1950s, White men set laws against biracial marriage. There were no consequences for a White man raping a Black woman. Nor were there laws against a White man for raping his wife; plus there was no domestic violence law on the books.

Women are not completely blameless in all of this either because for thousands of years although most women today won't admit to it, power is seductive to them. Many women will get with a man just because of his power, whether he is an asshole, a fondler, or a womanizer. That behavior still holds true to this day and the proof of that is that over 30 million women in this country knowingly voted for such a man to lead this country in 2016, and they are on the verge of doing it again.

But today women can now use their newfound power. If a man hits her, or if a man rapes her, even if it's her husband she can put his ass in jail for a long time.

Women here in America can thank people like Gloria Allred, an attorney, Elizabeth Geddes, a prosecutor, and Maurene Comey, also a prosecutor for standing up for and fighting for their rights. Where were these strong White women when White men were taking and raping Black slave women?

Yes it was a different America back then but it is refreshing to know that there are White men today who understand right from wrong. Men like Richard Cellini of Georgetown, Dr. Adam Rothman, He Too of Georgetown, Gavin Newsom, Governor of

California, and all their many very capable staff members are leading the way to right some of the wrongs perpetrated in the past by White men against Black people.

Just a Little Footnote:

It is said by many that money is the root of all evil. So if that's true, I will submit to you that it is, Pussy and young boys' Dicks and Asses that are vying for a close second!

Unfortunately there will still be more rapes and more murders before the man gets it right. What we all as civilized individuals can do is just pray, stay on guard, stay out of harm's way and hope that if there is a God, that He or She comes to their senses and come down here and straighten this shit out before it's too late!